GEORGIA

Coordinate **Algebra**
Volume 2

Randall I. Charles
Basia Hall
Dan Kennedy
Laurie E. Bass
Allan E. Bellman
Sadie Chavis Bragg
William G. Handlin
Art Johnson
Stuart J. Murphy
Grant Wiggins

PEARSON

Boston, Massachusetts • Chandler, Arizona • Glenview, Illinois • Upper Saddle River, New Jersey

Acknowledgments appear on page Z42, which constitutes an extension of this copyright page.

PEARSON

ISBN-13:   978-0-13-323373-5
ISBN-10:   0-13-323373-1
2 3 4 5 6 7 8 9 10 V069 17 16 15 14 13

From the *Authors*

Welcome

Math is a powerful tool with far-reaching applications throughout your life. We have designed a unique and engaging program that will enable you to tap into the power of mathematics and mathematical reasoning. This award-winning program has been developed to align fully to the Common Core State Standards.

Developing mathematical understanding and problem-solving abilities is an ongoing process—a journey both inside and outside the classroom. This course is designed to help make sense of the mathematics you encounter in and out of class each day and to help you develop mathematical proficiency.

You will learn important mathematical principles. You will also learn how the principles are connected to one another and to what you already know. You will learn to solve problems and learn the reasoning that lies behind your solutions. You will also develop the key mathematical practices of the Common Core State Standards.

Each chapter begins with the "big ideas" of the chapter and some essential questions that you will learn to answer. Through this question-and-answer process you will develop your ability to analyze problems independently and solve them in different applications.

Your skills and confidence will increase through practice and review. Work through the problems so you understand the concepts and methods presented and the thinking behind them. Then do the exercises. Ask yourself how new concepts relate to old ones. Make the connections!

Everyone needs help sometimes. You will find that this program has built-in opportunities, both in this text and online, to get help whenever you need it.

The problem-solving and reasoning habits and problem-solving skills you develop in this program will serve you in all your studies and in your daily life. They will prepare you for future success not only as a student, but also as a member of a changing technological society.

Best wishes,

Series *Authors*

Randall I. Charles, Ph.D., is Professor Emeritus in the Department of Mathematics at San Jose State University, San Jose, California. He began his career as a high school mathematics teacher, and he was a mathematics supervisor for five years. Dr. Charles has been a member of several NCTM committees including the writing team for the Curriculum Focal Points. He is the former Vice President of the National Council of Supervisors of Mathematics. Much of his writing and research has been in the area of problem solving. He has authored more than 90 mathematics textbooks for kindergarten through college.

Dan Kennedy, Ph.D., is a classroom teacher and the Lupton Distinguished Professor of Mathematics at the Baylor School in Chattanooga, Tennessee. A frequent speaker at professional meetings on the subject of mathematics education reform, Dr. Kennedy has conducted more than 50 workshops and institutes for high school teachers. He is coauthor of textbooks in calculus and precalculus, and from 1990 to 1994 he chaired the College Board's AP Calculus Development Committee. He is a 1992 Tandy Technology Scholar and a 1995 Presidential Award winner.

Basia Hall currently serves as Manager of Instructional Programs for the Houston Independent School District. With 33 years of teaching experience, Ms. Hall has served as a department chair, instructional supervisor, school improvement facilitator, and professional development trainer. She has developed curricula for Algebra 1, Geometry, and Algebra 2 and co-developed the Texas state mathematics standards. A 1992 Presidential Awardee, Ms. Hall is past president of the Texas Association of Supervisors of Mathematics and is a state representative for the National Council of Supervisors of Mathematics (NCSM).

Consulting *Authors*

Stuart J. Murphy is a visual learning author and consultant. He is a champion of helping students develop visual learning skills so they become more successful students. He is the author of MathStart, a series of children's books that presents mathematical concepts in the context of stories, and *I See I Learn*, a Pre-Kindergarten and Kindergarten learning initiative that focuses on social and emotional skills. A graduate of the Rhode Island School of Design, he has worked extensively in educational publishing and has been on the authorship teams of a number of elementary and high school mathematics programs. He is a frequent presenter at meetings of the National Council of Teachers of Mathematics, the International Reading Association, and other professional organizations.

Grant Wiggins, Ed.D., is the President of Authentic Education in Hopewell, New Jersey. He earned his B.A. from St. John's College in Annapolis and his Ed.D. from Harvard University Dr. Wiggins consults with schools, districts, and state education departments on a variety of reform matters; organizes conferences and workshops; and develops print materials and web resources on curricular change. He is perhaps best known for being the coauthor, with Jay McTighe, of *Understanding by Design* and *The Understanding by Design Handbook*[1], the award-winning and highly successful materials on curriculum published by ASCD. His work has been supported by the Pew Charitable Trusts, the Geraldine R. Dodge Foundation, and the National Science Foundation.

[1] ASCD, publisher of the "Understanding by Design Handbook" co-authored by Grant Wiggins and registered owner of the trademark "Understanding by Design", has not authorized or sponsored this work and is in no way affiliated with Pearson or its products.

Program *Authors*

Algebra Topics

Allan E. Bellman, Ph.D., is an Associate Professor of Mathematics Education at the University of Mississippi. He previously taught at the University of California, Davis for 12 years and in public school in Montgomery County, Maryland for 31. He has been an instructor for both the Woodrow Wilson National Fellowship Foundation and the Texas Instruments' T^3 program. Dr. Bellman has expertise in the use of technology in education and assessment-driven instruction and speaks frequently on these topics. He is a recipient of the Tandy Award for Teaching Excellence and has twice been listed in Who's Who Among America's Teachers.

Sadie Chavis Bragg, Ed.D., is Senior Vice President of Academic Affairs and professor of mathematics at the Borough of Manhattan Community College of the City University of New York. She is a past president of the American Mathematical Association of Two-Year Colleges (AMATYC). In recognition for her service to the field of mathematics locally, statewide, nationally, and internationally, she was awarded AMATYC's most prestigious award, The Mathematics Excellence Award for 2010. Dr. Bragg has coauthored more than 60 mathematics textbooks for kindergarten through college.

William G. Handlin, Sr., is a classroom teacher and Department Chair of Mathematics and former Department Chair of Technology Applications at Spring Woods High School in Houston, Texas. Awarded Life Membership in the Texas Congress of Parents and Teachers for his contributions to the well-being of children, Mr. Handlin is also a frequent workshop and seminar leader in professional meetings.

Geometry Topics

Laurie E. Bass is a classroom teacher at the 9–12 division of the Ethical Culture Fieldston School in Riverdale, New York. A classroom teacher for more than 30 years, Ms. Bass has a wide base of teaching experiences, ranging from Grade 6 through Advanced Placement Calculus. She was the recipient of a 2000 Honorable Mention for the Radio Shack National Teacher Awards. She has been a contributing writer for a number of publications, including software-based activities for the Algebra 1 classroom. Among her areas of special interest are cooperative learning for high school students and geometry exploration on the computer. Ms. Bass is a frequent presenter at local, regional, and national conferences.

Art Johnson, Ed.D., is a professor of mathematics education at Boston University. He is a mathematics educator with 32 years of public school teaching experience, a frequent speaker and workshop leader, and the recipient of a number of awards: the Tandy Prize for Teaching Excellence, the Presidential Award for Excellence in Mathematics Teaching, and New Hampshire Teacher of the Year. He was also profiled by the Disney Corporation in the American Teacher of the Year Program. Dr. Johnson has contributed 18 articles to NCTM journals and has authored over 50 books on various aspects of mathematics.

Using **Your Book** *with Success*

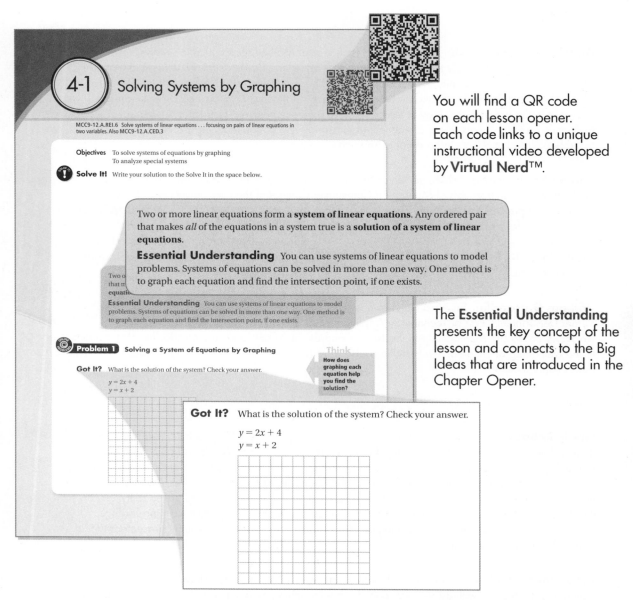

4-1   Solving Systems by Graphing

MCC9-12.A.REI.6 Solve systems of linear equations . . . focusing on pairs of linear equations in two variables. Also MCC9-12.A.CED.3

Objectives   To solve systems of equations by graphing
                To analyze special systems

Solve It!   Write your solution to the Solve It in the space below.

Two or more linear equations form a **system of linear equations**. Any ordered pair that makes *all* of the equations in a system true is a **solution of a system of linear equations**.

Essential Understanding   You can use systems of linear equations to model problems. Systems of equations can be solved in more than one way. One method is to graph each equation and find the intersection point, if one exists.

Problem 1   Solving a System of Equations by Graphing

Got It?   What is the solution of the system? Check your answer.
$$y = 2x + 4$$
$$y = x + 2$$

Think

How does graphing each equation help you find the solution?

Got It?   What is the solution of the system? Check your answer.
$$y = 2x + 4$$
$$y = x + 2$$

You will find a QR code on each lesson opener. Each code links to a unique instructional video developed by **Virtual Nerd**™.

The **Essential Understanding** presents the key concept of the lesson and connects to the Big Ideas that are introduced in the Chapter Opener.

After working through the Problem in the Interactive Digital Path, you complete a **Got It?** exercise in your book. For exercises that require graphing, a blank grid is provided.

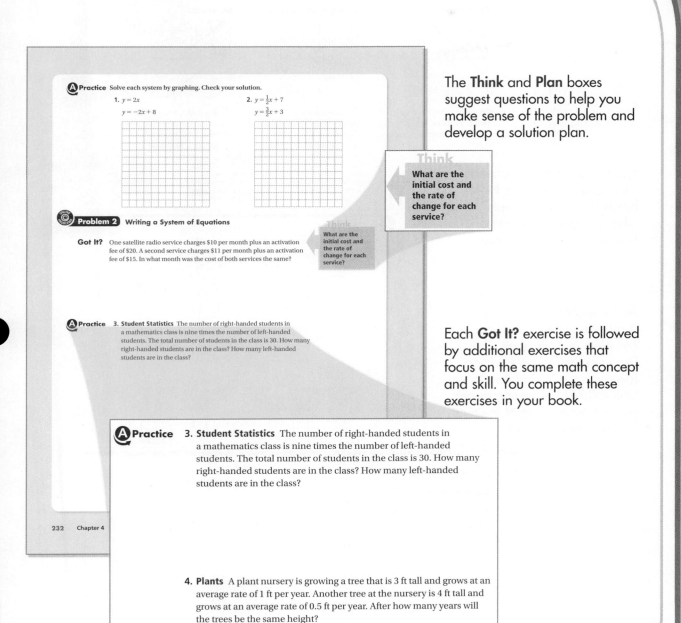

The **Think** and **Plan** boxes suggest questions to help you make sense of the problem and develop a solution plan.

Practice Solve each system by graphing. Check your solution.

1. $y = 2x$
   $y = -2x + 8$

2. $y = \frac{1}{2}x + 7$
   $y = \frac{3}{2}x + 3$

Problem 2 Writing a System of Equations

Got It? One satellite radio service charges $10 per month plus an activation fee of $20. A second service charges $11 per month plus an activation fee of $15. In what month was the cost of both services the same?

Think
What are the initial cost and the rate of change for each service?

Think
What are the initial cost and the rate of change for each service?

Practice 3. **Student Statistics** The number of right-handed students in a mathematics class is nine times the number of left-handed students. The total number of students in the class is 30. How many right-handed students are in the class? How many left-handed students are in the class?

Each **Got It?** exercise is followed by additional exercises that focus on the same math concept and skill. You complete these exercises in your book.

Practice 3. **Student Statistics** The number of right-handed students in a mathematics class is nine times the number of left-handed students. The total number of students in the class is 30. How many right-handed students are in the class? How many left-handed students are in the class?

4. **Plants** A plant nursery is growing a tree that is 3 ft tall and grows at an average rate of 1 ft per year. Another tree at the nursery is 4 ft tall and grows at an average rate of 0.5 ft per year. After how many years will the trees be the same height?

take note

Concept Summary   Systems of Linear Equations

One solution	Infinitely many solutions	No solution
The lines intersect at one point. The lines have different slopes. The equations are consistent and independent.	The lines are the same. The lines have the same slope and y-intercept. The equations are consistent and dependent.	The lines are parallel. The lines have the same slope and different y-intercepts. The equations are inconsistent.

You can use the instructional summaries in the **Take Note** boxes to review concepts when completing homework or studying for an assessment.

The lines intersect at one point. The lines have different slopes. The equations are consistent and independent.	The lines are the same. The lines have the same slope and y-intercept. The equations are consistent and dependent.	The lines are parallel. The lines have the same slope and different y-intercepts. The equations are inconsistent.

 Lesson Check

Do you know HOW?

Solve each system by graphing.

7. $y = x + 7$
   $y = 2x + 1$

8. $y = \frac{1}{2}x + 6$
   $y = x - 2$

At the end of each lesson is a **Lesson Check** that you complete in your book. The Do you know HOW? section focuses on skills and the Do you UNDERSTAND? section targets your understanding of the math concepts related to the skills.

9. $y = -3x - 3$
   $y = 2x + 2$

10. $y = -x - 4$
    $4x - y = -1$

 Lesson Check

Do you know HOW?

Solve each system by graphing.

7. $y = x + 7$
   $y = 2x + 1$

8. $y = \frac{1}{2}x + 6$
   $y = x - 2$

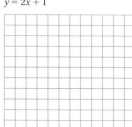

More Practice and Problem-Solving Exercises

 MATHEMATICAL
PRACTICES

Ⓑ Apply

13. Money You have a jar of pennies and quarters. You want to choose 15 coins that are worth exactly $4.35.
  a. Write and solve a system of equations that models the situation.
  b. Is your solution reasonable in terms of the original problem? Explain.

Solve each system. Explain why you chose the method you used.

14. $4x + 5y = 3$
$3x - 2y = 8$

15. $2x + 7y = -20$
$y = 3x + 7$

16. $5x + 2y = 17$
$x - 2y = 8$

Each lesson ends with **More Practice and Problem Solving** Exercises. You will complete these exercises in your homework notebook or on a separate sheet of paper.

The exercises with the **Common Core logo** help you become more proficient with the Standards for Mathematical Practice.

Those with **STEM** logo provide practice with science, technology, or engineering topics.

More Practice and Problem-Solving Exercises

 MATHEMATICAL
PRACTICES

Ⓑ Apply

13. Money You have a jar of pennies and quarters. You want to choose 15 coins that are worth exactly $4.35.
  a. Write and solve a system of equations that models the situation.
  b. Is your solution reasonable in terms of the original problem? Explain.

Solve each system. Explain why you chose the method you used.

14. $4x + 5y = 3$
$3x - 2y = 8$

15. $2x + 7y = -20$
$y = 3x + 7$

16. $5x + 2y = 17$
$x - 2y = 8$

Ⓒ **17. Reasoning** Find A and B so that the system below has the solution (2, 3).
$Ax - 2By = 6$
$3Ax - By = -12$

Ⓒ **18. Think About a Plan** A tugboat can pull a boat 24 mi downstream in 2 h. Going upstream, the tugboat can pull the same boat 16 mi in 2 h. What is the speed of the tugboat in still water? What is the speed of the current?
  • How can you use the formula $d = rt$ to help you solve the problem?
  • How are the tugboat's speeds when traveling upstream and downstream related to its speed in still water and the speed of the current?

Ⓒ **Open-Ended** Without solving, decide which method you would use to solve each system: graphing, substitution, or elimination. Explain.

19. $y = 3x - 1$
$y = 4x$

20. $3m - 4n = 1$
$3m - 2n = -1$

21. $4s - 3t = 8$
$t = -2s - 1$

22. Business A perfume maker has stocks of two perfumes on hand. Perfume A sells for $15 per ounce. Perfume B sells for $35 per ounce. How much of each should be combined to make a 3-oz bottle of perfume that can be sold for $63?

STEM 23. Chemistry In a chemistry lab, you have two vinegars. One is 5% acetic acid, and one is 6.5% acetic acid. You want to make 200 mL of a vinegar with 6% acetic acid. How many milliliters of each vinegar do you need to mix together?

24. Boating A boat is traveling in a river with a current that has a speed of 1.5 km/h. In one hour, the boat can travel twice the distance downstream that it can travel upstream. What is the boat's speed in still water?

What is a **QR code** and how do I use it?

A unique feature of Pearson's *Georgia High School Mathematics* is the QR code on every lesson opener. QR codes can be scanned by any electronic device with a camera, such as a smart phone, tablet, and even some laptop computers. The QR codes on the lesson openers link to Virtual Nerd™ tutorial videos that directly relate to the content in the lesson. To learn more about Virtual Nerd tutorial videos and its exclusive dynamic whiteboard, go to virtualnerd.com.

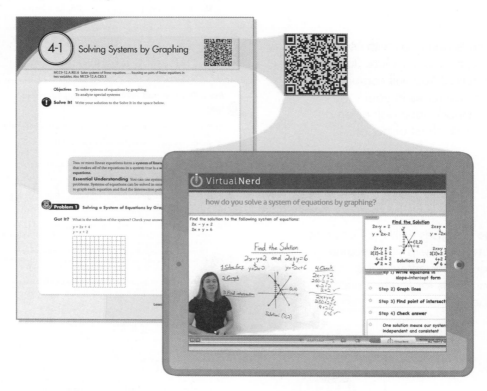

You must have a QR code reader on your mobile device or computer. You can download a QR reader app at the app store for your mobile device.

Step 1: Go to the app store for your camera-enabled smart phone or tablet.

Step 2: Search for "QR" or "QR readers". Download the QR reader app.

Step 3: Open that app and follow the instructions to scan. Whenever you want to scan a QR code, you will need to open the QR reader app first, otherwise you will just end up taking a picture of a QR code.

Step 4: After scanning the QR code, the appropriate Virtual Nerd tutorial video will play.

What **Resources** can I use when studying?

Pearson's *Georgia High School Mathematics* offers a range of resources that you can use out of class.

Student Worktext Your book is more than a textbook. Not only does it have important summaries of key math concepts and skills, it will also have your worked-out solutions to the *Got It?* and *Practice* exercises and your own notes for each lesson or problem. Use your book to:

- Refer back to your worked-out solutions and notes.

- Review the key concepts of each lesson by rereading the *Essential Understanding* and *Take Note* boxes.

- Access video tutorials of the concepts addressed in the lesson by scanning the QR codes.

Pearson SuccessNet You have full access to all of the resources on Pearson SuccessNet, including the **Interactive Digital Path** where you will find all of the *Solve Its!* and Problems presented in class. Revisit the animated, stepped-out problems presented in-class to clarify and solidify your math knowledge. Additional resources available to you include:

- Interactive Student Worktext
- Homework Video Tutors in English and Spanish
- Online Glossary with audio in English and Spanish
- MathXL for School Interactive Math Practice
- Math Tools and Online Manipulatives
- Multilingual Handbook
- Assessments with immediate feedback

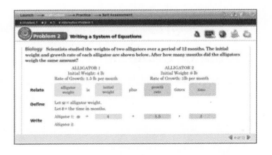

Mobile eText You may wish to access your student book on the go, either online or offline via download. Pearson's *Georgia High School Mathematics* also offers you a complete mobile etext of the Student Worktext.

- Use the notes, highlight, and bookmark features to personalize your eText.

- Watch animated problem videos with step-by-step instruction for every lesson.

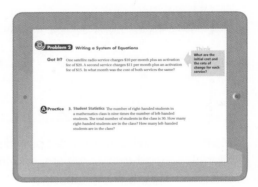

Pearson SuccessNet

Pearson SuccessNet is the gateway to all of the digital components of the program. You can use the online content to review the day's lesson, complete lessons independently, get help with your homework assignments, and prepare for and/or take an assessment. You will be given a username and password to log into www.pearsonsuccessnet.com.

The Homepage

Your eText includes links to animated lesson videos, highlighting and note taking tools, and a visual glossary with audio.

The **To Do** tab contains a list of assignments that you need to complete. You can also access your gradebook and review past assignments.

The **Explore** tab provides you access to the Table of Contents and all of the digital content for the program.

You can also access the following student resources: Practice Worksheets, Homework Video Tutors, and a Multilingual Handbook

Table of Contents

To access the Table of Contents, click on *Explore* from your Homepage.

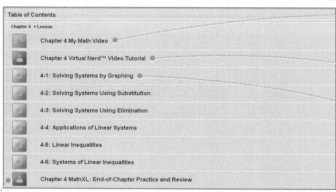

Student-developed videos bring real-life context to mathematics.

Step-by-step video tutorials offer additional support for every lesson.

Digital lessons include access to animated problems, math tools, homework exercises, and self-assessments.

MathXL for School exercises provide additional practice. Examples and tutorials support every problem, and instant feedback is provided as you complete each exercise.

Interactive Digital Path

To access the **Interactive Digital Path**, click on the appropriate lesson from the Table of Contents.

Math Tools help you explore and visualize concepts.

You'll find opportunities to review formulas, properties, and other key concepts.

Interactive Glossary is available in English and Spanish with audio.

Every lesson includes the following:

Launch: Interactive lesson opener connects the math to real-world applications.

Instruction: All lesson problems are stepped out with detailed instruction. You can complete the subsequent *Got It?* exercises in your Student Worktext.

Practice: Exercises from your Student Worktext are available for view.

Self-Assessment: You can take the self-check lesson quiz, and then check your answers on the second screen.

MathXL for School

To access *MathXL for School,* click on the Chapter Review and Practice link from the Table of Contents.

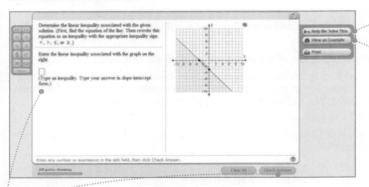

Select **Help Me Solve This** for an interactive step-by-step tutorial.

Select **View an Example** to see a similar worked out problem.

Input your answer and select **Check Answer** to get immediate feedback. After completing the exercise, a new exercise automatically regenerates, so you have unlimited practice opportunities.

Common Core
State Standards
Coordinate Algebra

Number and Quantity

Quantities

Reason quantitatively and use units to solve problems

N.Q.1	Use units as a way to understand problems and to guide the solution of multi-step problems; choose and interpret units consistently in formulas; choose and interpret the scale and the origin in graphs and data displays. ★
N.Q.2	Define appropriate quantities for the purpose of descriptive modeling. ★
N.Q.3	Choose a level of accuracy appropriate to limitations on measurement when reporting quantities. ★

Algebra

Seeing Structure in Expressions

Interpret the structure of expressions

A.SSE.1.a	Interpret expressions that represent a quantity in terms of its content. Interpret parts of an expression, such as terms, factors, and coefficients. ★
A.SSE.1.b	Interpret expressions that represent a quantity in terms of its content. Interpret complicated expressions by viewing one or more of their parts as a single entity. *For example, interpret $P(1 + r)^n$ as the product of P and a factor not depending on P.* ★

Creating Equations

Create equations that describe numbers or relationships

A.CED.1	Create equations and inequalities in one variable and use them to solve problems. ★ *Include equations arising from linear and exponential functions.*
A.CED.2	Create equations in two or more variables to represent relationships between quantities; graph equations on coordinate axes with labels and scales. ★
A.CED.3	Represent constraints by equations or inequalities, and by systems of equations and/or inequalities, and interpret solutions as viable or nonviable options in a modeling context. *For example, represent inequalities describing nutritional and cost constraints on combinations of different foods.* ★
A.CED.4	Rearrange formulas to highlight a quantity of interest, using the same reasoning as in solving equations. *For example, rearrange Ohm's law $V = IR$ to highlight resistance R.* ★

Reasoning with Equations and Inequalities

Understand solving equations as a process of reasoning and explain the reasoning

A.REI.1	Explain each step in solving a simple equation as following from the equality of numbers asserted at the previous step, starting from the assumption that the original equation has a solution. Construct a viable argument to justify a solution method.

Solve equations and inequalities in one variable

A.REI.3	Solve linear equations and inequalities in one variable, including equations with coefficients represented by letters.

Solve systems of equations

A.REI.5	Prove that, given a system of two equations in two variables, replacing one equation by the sum of that equation and a multiple of the other produces a system with the same solutions.
A.REI.6	Solve systems of linear equations exactly and approximately (e.g., with graphs), focusing on pairs of linear equations in two variables.

Represent and solve equations and inequalities graphically

A.REI.10   Understand that the graph of an equation in two variables is the set of all its solutions plotted in the coordinate plane, often forming a curve (which could be a line).

A.REI.11   Explain why the x-coordinates of the points where the graphs of the equations $y = f(x)$ and $y = g(x)$ intersect are the solutions of the equation $f(x) = g(x)$; find the solutions approximately, e.g., using technology to graph the functions, make tables of values, or find successive approximations. *Include cases where f(x) and/or g(x) are linear and exponential functions.* ★

A.REI.12   Graph the solutions to a linear inequality in two variables as a half-plane (excluding the boundary in the case of a strict inequality), and graph the solution set to a system of linear inequalities in two variables as the intersection of the corresponding half-planes.

Functions

Interpreting Functions

Understand the concept of a function and use function notation

F.IF.1   Understand that a function from one set (called the domain) to another set (called the range) assigns to each element of the domain exactly one element of the range. If f is a function and x is an element of its domain, then $f(x)$ denotes the output of f corresponding to the input x. The graph of f is the graph of the equation $y = f(x)$.

F.IF.2   Use function notation, evaluate functions for inputs in their domains, and interpret statements that use function notation in terms of a context.

F.IF.3   Recognize that sequences are functions, sometimes defined recursively, whose domain is a subset of the integers. *For example, the Fibonacci sequence is defined recursively by $f(0) = f(1) = 1$, $f(n + 1) = f(n) + f(n −1)$ for $n ≥ 1$ (n is greater than or equal to 1).*

Interpret functions that arise in applications in terms of the context

F.IF.4   For a function that models a relationship between two quantities, interpret key features of graphs and tables in terms of the quantities, and sketch graphs showing key features given a verbal description of the relationship. *Key features include: intercepts; intervals where the function is increasing, decreasing, positive, or negative; relative maximums and minimums; symmetries; end behavior.* ★

F.IF.5   Relate the domain of a function to its graph and, where applicable, to the quantitative relationship it describes. *For example, if the function h(n) gives the number of person-hours it takes to assemble n engines in a factory, then the positive integers would be an appropriate domain for the function.* ★

F.IF.6   Calculate and interpret the average rate of change of a function (presented symbolically or as a table) over a specified interval. Estimate the rate of change from a graph. ★

Analyze functions using different representations

F.IF.7.a   Graph functions expressed symbolically and show key features of the graph, by hand in simple cases and using technology for more complicated cases. Graph linear functions and show intercepts, maxima, and minima. ★

F.IF.7.e   Graph functions expressed symbolically and show key features of the graph, by hand in simple cases and using technology for more complicated cases. Graph exponential functions, showing intercepts and end behavior. ★

F.IF.9   Compare properties of two functions each represented in a different way (algebraically, graphically, numerically in tables, or by verbal descriptions). *For example, given a graph of one quadratic function and an algebraic expression for another, say which has the larger maximum.*

Building Functions

Build a function that models a relationship between two quantities

F.BF.1.a   Write a function that describes a relationship between two quantities. ★ Determine an explicit expression, a recursive process, or steps for calculation from a context.

F.BF.1.b	Write a function that describes a relationship between two quantities. ★ Combine standard function types using arithmetic operations. *For example, build a function that models the temperature of a cooling body by adding a constant function to a decaying exponential, and relate these functions to the model.*
F.BF.2	Write arithmetic and geometric sequences both recursively and with an explicit formula, use them to model situations, and translate between the two forms. ★

Build new functions from existing functions

F.BF.3	Identify the effect on the graph of replacing $f(x)$ by $f(x) + k$, $k\,f(x)$, $f(kx)$, and $f(x + k)$ for specific values of k (both positive and negative); find the value of k given the graphs. Experiment with cases and illustrate an explanation of the effects on the graph using technology. *Include recognizing even and odd functions from their graphs and algebraic expressions for them.*

Linear, Quadratic, and Exponential Models

Construct and compare linear and exponential models and solve problems.

F.LE.1.a	Distinguish between situations that can be modeled with linear functions and with exponential functions. Prove that linear functions grow by equal differences over equal intervals, and that exponential functions grow by equal factors over equal intervals. ★
F.BF.1.b	Distinguish between situations that can be modeled with linear functions and with exponential functions. Recognize situations in which one quantity changes at a constant rate per unit interval relative to another. ★
F.LE.1.c	Distinguish between situations that can be modeled with linear functions and with exponential functions. Recognize situations in which a quantity grows or decays by a constant percent rate per unit interval relative to another. ★
F.LE.2	Construct linear and exponential functions, including arithmetic and geometric sequences, given a graph, a description of a relationship, or two input-output pairs (include reading these from a table). ★
F.LE.3	Observe using graphs and tables that a quantity increasing exponentially eventually exceeds a quantity increasing linearly. ★

Interpret expressions for functions in terms of the situation they model

F.LE.5	Interpret the parameters in a linear or exponential function in terms of a context. ★

Look at the domains in bold and the clusters to get a good idea of the topics you'll study this year.

Geometry

Congruence

Experiment with Transformations in the Plane

G.CO.1	Know precise definitions of angle, circle, perpendicular line, parallel line, and line segment, based on the undefined notions of point, line, distance along a line, and distance around a circular arc.
G.CO.2	Represent transformations in the plane using, e.g., transparencies and geometry software; describe transformations as functions that take points in the plane as inputs and give other points as outputs. Compare transformations that preserve distance and angle to those that do not (e.g., translation versus horizontal stretch).
G.CO.3	Given a rectangle, parallelogram, trapezoid, or regular polygon, describe the rotations and reflections that carry it onto itself.
G.CO.4	Develop definitions of rotations, reflections, and translations in terms of angles, circles, perpendicular lines, parallel lines, and line segments.
G.CO.5	Given a geometric figure and a rotation, reflection, or translation, draw the transformed figure using, e.g., graph paper, tracing paper, or geometry software. Specify a sequence of transformations that will carry a given figure onto another.

Expressing Geometric Properties with Equations

Use coordinates to prove simple geometric theorems algebraically.

G.GPE.4	Use coordinates to prove simple geometric theorems algebraically.
G.GPE.5	Prove the slope criteria for parallel and perpendicular lines and use them to solve geometric problems (e.g., find the equation of a line parallel or perpendicular to a given line that passes through a given point).
G.GPE.6	Find the point on a directed line segment between two given points that partitions the segment in a given ratio.
G.GPE.7	Use coordinates to compute perimeters of polygons and areas of triangles and rectangles, e.g., using the distance formula.★

Statistics and Probability

Interpreting Categorical and Quantitative Data

Summarize, represent, and interpret data on a single count or measurement variable

S.ID.1	Represent data with plots on the real number line (dot plots, histograms, and box plots).★
S.ID.2	Use statistics appropriate to the shape of the data distribution to compare center (median, mean) and spread (interquartile range) of two or more different data sets.★
S.ID.3	Interpret differences in shape, center, and spread in the context of the data sets, accounting for possible effects of extreme data points (outliers).★

Summarize, represent, and interpret data on two categorical and quantitative variables

S.ID.5	Summarize categorical data for two categories in two-way frequency tables. Interpret relative frequencies in the context of the data (including joint, marginal, and conditional relative frequencies). Recognize possible associations and trends in the data.★
S.ID.6.a	Represent data on two quantitative variables on a scatter plot, and describe how the variables are related. Fit a function to the data; use functions fitted to data to solve problems in the context of the data. Use given functions or choose a function suggested by the context. Emphasize linear and exponential models.★
S.ID.6.b	Represent data on two quantitative variables on a scatter plot, and describe how the variables are related. Informally assess the fit of a function by plotting and analyzing residuals.★
S.ID.6.c	Represent data on two quantitative variables on a scatter plot, and describe how the variables are related. Fit a linear function for a scatter plot that suggests a linear association.★

Interpret linear models

S.ID.7	Interpret the slope (rate of change) and the intercept (constant term) of a linear model in the context of the data.★
S.ID.8	Compute (using technology) and interpret the correlation coefficient of a linear fit.★
S.ID.9	Distinguish between correlation and causation.★

BIGideas

These Big Ideas are the organizing ideas for the study of important areas of mathematics: algebra, geometry, and statistics.

Stay connected! These Big Ideas will help you understand how the math you study in high school fits together.

Algebra

Properties
- In the transition from arithmetic to algebra, attention shifts from arithmetic operations (addition, subtraction, multiplication, and division) to the use of the *properties* of these operations.
- All of the facts of arithmetic and algebra follow from certain properties.

Variable
- Quantities are used to form expressions, equations, and inequalities.
- An expression refers to a quantity but does not make a statement about it. An equation (or an inequality) is a statement about the quantities it mentions.
- Using variables in place of numbers in equations (or inequalities) allows the statement of relationships among numbers that are unknown or unspecified.

Equivalence
- A single quantity may be represented by many different expressions.
- The facts about a quantity may be expressed by many different equations (or inequalities).

Solving Equations & Inequalities
- Solving an equation is the process of rewriting the equation to make what it says about its variable(s) as simple as possible.
- Properties of numbers and equality can be used to transform an equation (or inequality) into equivalent, simpler equations (or inequalities) in order to find solutions.
- Useful information about equations and inequalities (including solutions) can be found by analyzing graphs or tables.
- The numbers and types of solutions vary predictably, based on the type of equation.

Proportionality
- Two quantities are *proportional* if they have the same ratio in each instance where they are measured together.
- Two quantities are *inversely proportional* if they have the same product in each instance where they are measured together.

Function
- A function is a relationship between variables in which each value of the input variable is associated with a unique value of the output variable.
- Functions can be represented in a variety of ways, such as graphs, tables, equations, or words. Each representation is particularly useful in certain situations.
- Some important families of functions are developed through transformations of the simplest form of the function.
- New functions can be made from other functions by applying arithmetic operations or by applying one function to the output of another.

Modeling
- Many real-world mathematical problems can be represented algebraically. These representations can lead to algebraic solutions.
- A function that models a real-world situation can be used to make estimates or predictions about future occurrences.

Statistics and Probability

Data Collection and Analysis
- Sampling techniques are used to gather data from real-world situations. If the data are representative of the larger population, inferences can be made about that population.
- Biased sampling techniques yield data unlikely to be representative of the larger population.
- Sets of numerical data are described using measures of central tendency and dispersion.

Data Representation
- The most appropriate data representations depend on the type of data—quantitative or qualitative, and univariate or bivariate.
- Line plots, box plots, and histograms are different ways to show distribution of data over a possible range of values.

Probability
- Probability expresses the likelihood that a particular event will occur.
- Data can be used to calculate an experimental probability, and mathematical properties can be used to determine a theoretical probability.
- Either experimental or theoretical probability can be used to make predictions or decisions about future events.
- Various counting methods can be used to develop theoretical probabilities.

Geometry

Visualization
- Visualization can help you see the relationships between two figures and help you connect properties of real objects with two-dimensional drawings of these objects.

Transformations
- Transformations are mathematical functions that model relationships with figures.
- Transformations may be described geometrically or by coordinates.
- Symmetries of figures may be defined and classified by transformations.

Measurement
- Some attributes of geometric figures, such as length, area, volume, and angle measure, are measurable. Units are used to describe these attributes.

Reasoning & Proof
- Definitions establish meanings and remove possible misunderstanding.
- Other truths are more complex and difficult to see. It is often possible to verify complex truths by reasoning from simpler ones using deductive reasoning.

Similarity
- Two geometric figures are similar when corresponding lengths are proportional and corresponding angles are congruent.
- Areas of similar figures are proportional to the squares of their corresponding lengths.
- Volumes of similar figures are proportional to the cubes of their corresponding lengths.

Coordinate Geometry
- A coordinate system on a line is a number line on which points are labeled, corresponding to the real numbers.
- A coordinate system in a plane is formed by two perpendicular number lines, called the x- and y-axes, and the quadrants they form. The coordinate plane can be used to graph many functions.
- It is possible to verify some complex truths using deductive reasoning in combination with the distance, midpoint, and slope formulas.

6

Data Analysis

Get Ready!		**369**
Chapter Opener		**370**
6-1	Frequency and Histograms	371
6-2	Measures of Central Tendency and Dispersion	379
	Activity Lab 6-2a: Mean Absolute Deviation	388
	Lesson Lab 6-2b: Standard Deviation	390
6-3	Box-and-Whisker Plots	392
6-4	Scatter Plots and Trend Lines	399
	Activity Lab 6-4: Using Residuals	411
6-5	Two-Way Frequency Tables	414
Chapter Review		**425**
Pull It All Together		**428**

Chapter 6

Number and Quantity

Quantities
Reason quantitatively and use units to solve problems

Statistics and Probability

Interpreting Categorical and Quantitative Data
Summarize, represent, and interpret data on a single count or measurement variable

Summarize, represent, and interpret data on two categorical and quantitative variables

Interpret linear models.

Tools of Geometry

Get Ready!		**429**
Chapter Opener		**430**
7-1	Nets and Drawings for Visualizing Geometry	431
7-2	Points, Lines, and Planes	441
7-3	Measuring Segments	451
7-4	Measuring Angles	458
7-5	Exploring Angle Pairs	466
7-6	Midpoint and Distance in the Coordinate Plane	475
	Lesson Lab 7-6: Quadrilaterals and Other Polygons	483
Chapter Review		**487**
Pull It All Together		**490**

Chapter 7

Geometry

Congruence
Experiment with transformations in the plane.

Geometry

Expressing Geometric Properties with Equations
Use coordinates to prove simple geometric theorems algebraically

8

Transformations

Get Ready!		**491**
Chapter Opener		**492**
	Activity Lab 8-1: Tracing Paper Transformations	493
8-1	Translations	495
	Activity Lab 8-2: Paper Folding and Reflections	505
8-2	Reflections	507
8-3	Rotations	515
	Activity Lab 8-3: Symmetry	523
	Technology Lab 8-4: Exploring Multiple Transformations	529
8-4	Compositions of Isometries	532
Chapter Review		**540**
Pull It All Together		**542**

Geometry

Congruence
Experiment with transformations in the plane.

Chapter 8

Connecting Algebra and Geometry

Get Ready!		**543**
Chapter Opener		**544**
9-1	Perimeter and Area in the Coordinate Plane	545
	Lesson Lab 9-1: Partitioning a Segment	557
9-2	Areas of Parallelograms and Triangles	559
9-3	Areas of Trapezoids, Rhombuses, and Kites	568
	Activity Lab 9-4: Proving Slope Criteria for Parallel and Perpendicular Lines	575
9-4	Polygons in the Coordinate Plane	579
Chapter Review		**586**
Pull It All Together		**588**

Chapter 9

Number and Quantity
Quantities
   Reason quantitatively and use units to solve problems.

Geometry
Expressing Geometric Properties with Equations
   Use coordinates to prove simple geometric theorems algebraically.

This page intentionally left blank.

Get Ready!

Multiplying and Dividing Real Numbers

Simplify each fraction.

1. $\dfrac{6+4+7+9}{4}$ **2.** $\dfrac{1.7+4.2+3.1}{3}$ **3.** $\dfrac{11+16+9+12+7}{5}$

Distributive Property

Simplify each expression.

4. $6(x-7)$ **5.** $\frac{1}{2}(4x+6)$

6. $-2(5-x)$ **7.** $0.5(5+4x)$

Comparing Unit Rates

8. Transportation A car traveled 360 km in 6 h. A train traveled 400 km in 8 h. A boat traveled 375 km in 5 h. Which had the fastest average speed?

9. Plants A birch tree grew 2.5 in. in 5 months. A bean plant grew 8 in. in 10 months. A rose bush grew 5 in. in 8 months. Which grew the fastest?

Graphing a Function Rule

Make a table of values for each function rule. Then graph each function.

10. $f(x) = x + 3$ **11.** $f(x) = -2x$ **12.** $f(x) = x - 4$

 Looking Ahead Vocabulary

13. On a highway, the *median* is the strip of land that divides the two sides of opposing traffic. How would you expect a *median* to divide a data set?

14. *Percentiles* and *quartiles* are used to rank data divided into equal parts. How many equal parts do you think *quartiles* divide data into? How many equal parts do you think *percentiles* divide data into?

CHAPTER 6

Data Analysis

Big Ideas

1 Data Collection and Analysis
Essential Question How can collecting and analyzing data help you make decisions or predictions?

2 Data Representation
Essential Question How can you make and interpret different representations of data?

3 Modeling
Essential Question How can you make predictions based on a scatter plot?

©Domains

- Interpreting Categorical and Quantitative Data
- Quantities

Interactive Digital Path

Log in to **pearsonsuccessnet.com** and click on Interactive Digital Path to access the Solve Its and animated Problems.

Chapter Preview

6-1 Frequency and Histograms
6-2 Measures of Central Tendency and Dispersion
6-3 Box-and-Whisker Plots
6-4 Scatter Plots and Trend Lines
6-5 Two-Way Frequency Tables

Vocabulary

English/Spanish Vocabulary Audio Online:

English	Spanish
box-and-whisker plot, *p. 394*	gráfica de cajas
frequency table, *p. 371*	tabla de frecuencias
measure of central tendency, *p. 379*	medida de tendencia central
outlier, *p. 379*	valor extremo
percentile, *p. 395*	percentil
quartile, *p. 392*	cuartiles
range of a data set, *p. 382*	rango de un conjunto de datos
scatter plot, *p. 399*	diagrama de puntos
trend line, *p. 401*	línea de tendencia
two-way frequency table, *p. 414*	tabla de frecuencias de doble entrada

Frequency and Histograms

MCC9-12.S.ID.1 Represent data with plots on the real number line . . . Also MCC9-12.N.Q.1, MCC9-12.S.ID.3

Objective To make and interpret frequency tables and histograms

 **Solve It!** Write your solution to the Solve It in the space below.

Essential Understanding There are many ways to organize and visually display data. Sometimes it is helpful to organize numerical data into intervals.

The **frequency** of an interval is the number of data values in that interval. A **frequency table** groups a set of data values into intervals and shows the frequency for each interval. Intervals in frequency tables do not overlap, do not have any gaps, and are usually of equal size.

Problem 1 Making a Frequency Table

Got It? What is a frequency table for the data in Problem 1 that uses intervals of 5?

Think
Can there be more than one starting value for the first interval?

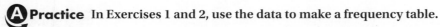 **Practice** In Exercises 1 and 2, use the data to make a frequency table.

      1. marathon times (min): 135 211 220 180 175 161
                                    246 201 192 167 235 208

      2. top speeds (mi/h): 108 90 96 150 120 115 135
                           126 165 155 130 125 100

A **histogram** is a graph that can display data from a frequency table. A histogram has one bar for each interval. The height of each bar shows the frequency of data in the interval it represents. There are no gaps between bars. The bars are usually of equal width.

Problem 2 **Making a Histogram**

Got It? The finishing times, in seconds, for a race are shown below. What is a histogram that represents the data?

       95 105 83 80 93 98 102 99 82 89 90 82 89

Plan

How can you use a frequency table to help make a histogram?

A **Practice** In Exercises 3 and 4, use the data to make a histogram.

3. restaurant waiting times (min): 20 35 15 25 5 10 40
30 10 50 20 60 10 8

4. points per game: 10 2 13 18 22 20 8 9 12
33 10 13 21 18 5 16 17 13

You can describe histograms in terms of their shape. Three types are shown below.

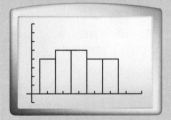

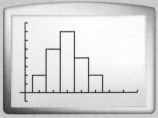

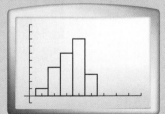

If the bars are roughly the same height, then the histogram is *uniform*.

If a vertical line can divide the histogram into two parts that are close to mirror images, then the histogram is *symmetric*.

If the histogram has one peak that is not in the center, then the histogram is *skewed*.

Problem 3 Interpreting Histograms

Got It?

a. The following set of data shows the numbers of dollars Jay spent on lunch over the last two weeks. Make a histogram of the data. Is the histogram *uniform*, *symmetric*, or *skewed*?

17 1 4 11 14 14 5 16 6 5 9 10 13 9

b. Reasoning How much money should Jay plan to bring for lunch next week? Explain your reasoning.

Practice Tell whether each histogram is *uniform*, *symmetric*, or *skewed*.

5.
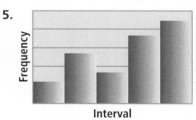

6.
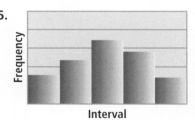

A **cumulative frequency** table shows the number of data values that lie in or below a given interval. For example, if the cumulative frequency for the interval 70–79 is 20, then there are 20 data values less than or equal to 79.

Problem 4   **Making a Cumulative Frequency Table**

Got It?   What is a cumulative frequency table that represents the data below?

12 13 15 1 5 7 10 9 2 2 7 11 2 1 0 15

Ⓐ Practice   **In Exercises 7 and 8, use the data to make a cumulative frequency table.**

7. heights of buildings (ft): 105 245 300 234 225 156
180 308 250 114 150 285

8. earthquake magnitudes: 2.1 5.4 6.7 3.2 4.5 2.7 2.6
3.1 4.4 8.1 4.1 2.9 2.1

Lesson Check

Do you know HOW?

The data below show battery life, in hours, for different brands of batteries.

12 9 10 14 10 11 10 18 21 10 14 22

9. Make a frequency table of the data.

10. Make a histogram of the data.

11. Make a cumulative frequency table of the data.

Do you UNDERSTAND?

12. Vocabulary How might a frequency table help a store owner determine the busiest business hours?

13. Compare and Contrast What is the difference between a symmetric histogram and a skewed histogram?

14. Writing How can you use a frequency table of a data set to construct a cumulative frequency table?

More Practice and Problem-Solving Exercises

 **Apply**

15. Music The Perpendicular Bisectors' new CD is shown at the right.
   a. Make a cumulative frequency table that represents the lengths of the songs in seconds.
   b. About what percent of the songs are under 4 min? How do you know?

Add It (intro)	1:25
A Fraction of My Love	3:30
Common Denominator	4:14
Always, Sometimes, Never	2:56
Factorial	3:15
Transitive Property	4:20
All You Need Is Math	4:58
SAS	3:51
Frequency	3:32
Subtract It (outro)	1:56

16. Think About a Plan A travel agent conducted a survey to find out how many times people go to the beach each year. The results of the survey are shown in the histogram at the right. About how many people were surveyed?

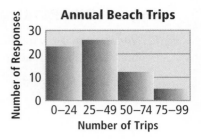
Annual Beach Trips

- What does the height of each bar represent?
- How can you use the bar heights to find the number of people surveyed?

Use the test scores below.

81 70 73 89 68 79 91 59 77 73 80 75 88 65 82 94 77 67 82

17. What is a histogram of the data that uses intervals of 5?

18. What is a histogram of the data that uses intervals of 10?

19. What is a histogram of the data that uses intervals of 20?

20. Reasoning Which interval size would you use—5, 10, or 20—to make it seem as though there were little variation in the test scores? Explain.

The histogram at the right shows the amounts of money that 50 customers spent in a supermarket.

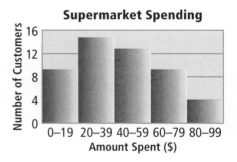
Supermarket Spending

21. What is the upper limit on the amount of money that any customer spent?

22. Which interval represents the greatest number of customers?

23. How many customers spent less than $20?

24. Writing Summarize the spending of the 50 customers represented in the histogram.

25. Error Analysis A student made the frequency table at the right using the data below. Describe and correct the error.

40 21 28 53 24 48 50 55 42 29 22 52 43 26 44

Interval	Frequency
20–29	6
40–49	5
50–59	4

**Challenge**

26. Make a histogram for a set of 200 data values. The histogram must have 40% of the values lie in the interval 20–29. The remaining values should be evenly divided among the intervals 0–9, 10–19, 30–39, and 40–49.

27. Copy and complete the cumulative frequency table below.

Interval	Frequency	Cumulative Frequency
0–9	■	6
10–19	■	17
20–29	■	26
30–39	■	35

6-2 Measures of Central Tendency and Dispersion

MCC9-12.S.ID.2 Use statistics appropriate to the shape of the data distribution to compare center . . . and spread . . . of two or more different data sets. Also MCC9-12.N.Q.2, MCC9-12.S.ID.1, MCC9-12.S.ID.3

Objective   To find mean, median, mode, and range

Solve It!   Write your solution to the Solve It in the space below.

Essential Understanding You can use different measures to interpret and compare sets of data.

One way to summarize a set of data is to use a *measure of central tendency*. Mean, median, and mode are all **measures of central tendency**.

The measure of central tendency that best describes a data set may depend on whether the data set has an *outlier*. An **outlier** is a data value that is much greater than or less than the other values in the set. Below is a review of mean, median, and mode, and when to use each as the measure of central tendency.

take note

Key Concept   Mean, Median, and Mode

Measure	When to Use
The **mean** equals $\frac{\text{sum of the data values}}{\text{total number of data values}}$. The mean is often referred to as the *average*.	Use mean to describe the middle of a set of data that *does not* have an outlier.
The **median** is the middle value in a data set when the values are arranged in order. For a set containing an even number of data values, the median is the mean of the two middle data values.	Use median to describe the middle of a set of data that *does* have an outlier.
The **mode** is the data item that occurs the most times. A data set can have no mode, one mode, or more than one mode.	Use mode when the data are nonnumeric or when choosing the most popular item.

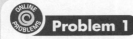 **Problem 1** **Finding Measures of Central Tendency**

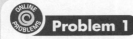

Got It? Consider the scores from Problem 1 that do not include the outlier, 189. What are the mean, median, and mode of the scores? Which measure of central tendency best describes the data?

> **Think**
>
> Which measure of central tendency is most affected by an outlier?

 Practice Find the mean, median, and mode of each data set. Tell which measure of central tendency best describes the data.

1. weights of books (oz): 12 10 9 15 16 10

2. golf scores: 98 96 98 134 99

You can use an equation to find a value needed to achieve a given average.

 **Problem 2** **Finding a Data Value**

Got It? **a.** The grades in Problem 2 were 80, 93, and 91. What grade would you need on your next exam to have an average of 88 on the four exams?

© **b. Reasoning** If 100 is the highest possible score on the fourth exam, is it possible to raise your average to 92? Explain.

Practice **3.** Find the value of x such that the data set 31.7, 42.8, 26.4, x has a mean of 35.

4. Sales The line plot at the right shows the numbers of weekly sales a salesperson made in the first nine weeks of a ten-week sales period. The salesperson's target is an average of 14 sales each week. How many sales does the salesperson need in the tenth week to meet the target average?

Number of Weekly Sales

		X	X
	X	X	X
X	X	X	X
12	13	14	15

A **measure of dispersion** describes how *dispersed*, or spread out, the values in a data set are. One measure of dispersion is *range*. The **range of a set of data** is the difference between the greatest and least data values.

 Problem 3 **Finding the Range**

Think

How do the purposes of the range and the mean differ?

Got It? For the same days, the closing prices, in dollars, of Stock C were 7, 4, 3, 6, and 1. The closing prices, in dollars, of Stock D were 24, 15, 2, 10, and 5. What are the range and mean of each set of data? Use your results to compare Stock C with Stock D.

 Practice **5.** Find the range and mean of each data set. Use your results to compare the two data sets.

Set E: 113 183 479 120 117
Set F: 145 129 153 135 142

6. Sports Over the past 6 seasons, one baseball player's batting averages were .265, .327, .294, .316, .281, and .318. A second player's batting averages were .304, .285, .312, .291, .303, and .314. What are the range and mean of each player's batting averages? Use your results to compare the players' batting skills.

A **line plot** is a data display in which each mark above a number line corresponds to each data value. Line plots are sometimes called *dot plots* when the mark used to represent each data value is a dot.

Problem 4 **Finding Measures of Central Tendency and Ranges**

Got It? The list below shows the number of students in each homeroom at Jefferson High School.

21, 22, 19, 20, 23, 21, 20, 24, 20, 19,
20, 21, 21, 23, 21, 22, 19, 21, 19, 20

a. Make a line plot of the data.

b. Find the mean, median, and range of the data.

c. How can you use the line plot to determine whether the mean and median are equal?

A Practice **7.** The list below shows the amount of time, in hours, one student spent on the Internet, per day, over a two week period. Make a line plot of the data. Then calculate the mean, median, mode, and range of the data.

3, 1, 4, 3, 2, 3, 2, 5, 6, 1, 3, 1, 3, 5

8. The list below shows ages of students on the math team. Make a line plot of the data. Then calculate the mean, median, mode, and range of the data.

14 14 15 15 16 15 15 16

 **Problem 5** **Comparing Measures of Central Tendency**

Got It?   Use the line plots from Problem 5 together with the results from a third class, shown here.

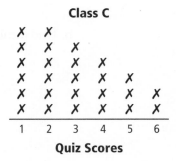

Class C

Quiz Scores

    a. Is the mean for Class C greater than or less than the mean for Class A?

    b. Is the median for Class C greater than or less than the median for Class A?

    c. How can you tell which data set has a greater mean by comparing the graphs?

Practice In Exercises 9 and 10, determine which data set has a greater mean and a greater median.

9.

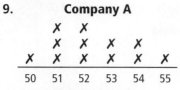

Company A

		X	X		
		X	X	X	
X	X	X	X	X	X
50	51	52	53	54	55

**Monthly Earnings
(thousands of dollars)**

Company B

		X	X	X	
		X	X	X	
X	X	X	X	X	X
50	51	52	53	54	55

**Monthly Earnings
(thousands of dollars)**

10.

Student A

					X
					X
				X	X
		X	X	X	X
	X	X	X	X	X
	X	X	X	X	X
X	X	X	X	X	X
X	X	X	X	X	X
30	31	32	33	34	35

Text Messages per Day

Student B

	X				
	X	X			
X	X	X	X		
X	X	X	X		
X	X	X	X		
X	X	X	X	X	
X	X	X	X	X	
X	X	X	X	X	
30	31	32	33	34	35

Text Messages per Day

 Lesson Check

Do you know HOW?

In Exercises 11 and 12, find the mean, median, and mode of each data set. Explain which measure best describes the data.

11. 1 29 33 31 30 33

12. 8.2 9.3 8.5 8.8 9.0

13. A student has gotten the following grades on his tests: 87, 95, 86, and 88. He needs to have an average of 90 to receive an A for the class. What is the minimum grade he must get on the last test in order to have an average of 90?

Do you UNDERSTAND?

14. Vocabulary How do mean, median, and mode describe the central tendency of a data set? Why are three different measures needed?

15. Error Analysis One student said 10 was the range of the data set 2, 10, 8, and 3. Another student said the range was 8. Which student is correct? Explain.

16. Reasoning How is the range of a data set affected by an outlier?

More Practice and Problem-Solving Exercises

Ⓑ Apply

Ⓒ **17. Reasoning** The mean of a data set is 7.8, the mode is 6.6, and the median is 6.8. What is the least possible number of data values in the set? Explain.

STEM **18. Manufacturing** Two manufacturing plants make sheets of steel for medical instruments. The back-to-back stem-and-leaf plot at the right shows data collected from the two plants.

   a. What are the mean, median, mode, and range of each data set?

   b. Which measure of central tendency best describes each data set? Explain.

   c. How can you use the shape of the back-to-back stem-and-leaf plot to determine which data set has the greater mean? Explain.

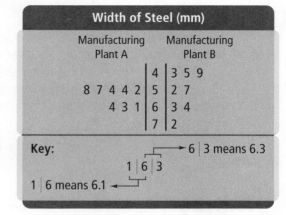

Width of Steel (mm)		
Manufacturing Plant A		Manufacturing Plant B
	4	3 5 9
8 7 4 4 2	5	2 7
4 3 1	6	3 4
	7	2

Key:

6 | 3 means 6.3

1 | 6 | 3

1 | 6 means 6.1

Ⓒ **19. Think About a Plan** The diameters of 5 circles are given below. What are the mean, median, mode, and range of the circumferences of the circles?

   6.5 in. 3.2 in. 7.4 in. 6.5 in. 5.8 in.

   • What are the mean, median, mode, and range of the diameters?

   • How do the mean, median, mode, and range change when the data change from diameters to circumferences?

Ⓒ **20. Reasoning** How does subtracting the same amount from each value in a data set affect the mean, median, mode, and range? Explain.

Ⓒ **21. Reasoning** How does dividing each value in a data set by the same nonzero amount affect the mean, median, mode, and range? Explain.

22. Wildlife Management A wildlife manager measured and tagged twelve adult male crocodiles. The data he collected are at the right. He estimates the crocodiles will grow 0.1 m each year. What will be the mean, median, mode, and range of the crocodiles' lengths after 4 yr?

Crocodile Lengths (m)			
2.4	2.5	2.5	2.3
2.8	2.4	2.3	2.4
2.1	2.2	2.5	2.7

Ⓒ **23. Reasoning** A friend tells you to apply for a sales job at a certain company because the salespeople earned an average of $47,500 last year. Last year, 6 salespeople earned $33,000, 3 earned $46,000, 2 earned $42,000, and 1 earned $150,000. Would you apply for the job based on what your friend says? Explain.

Ⓒ Challenge

24. Travel During the first 6 h of a car trip, your average speed is 44 mi/h. During the last 4 h of your trip, your average speed is 50 mi/h. What is your average speed for the whole trip? (*Hint:* First find the total number of miles traveled.)

25. Find the mean, median, mode, and range of the following algebraic expressions: $9x$, $4x$, $11x$, $7x$, $5x$, $4x$. Assume that $x > 0$.

Mean Absolute Deviation

MCC9-12.S.ID.2 Use statistics appropriate to the shape of the data distribution to compare . . . spread . . . of two or more different data sets.

The **mean absolute deviation (MAD)** of a data set describes how the values in the data set *deviate*, or differ, from the mean. You can use the MAD to determine how well the mean represents the data. Data sets that have a low MAD are more closely grouped around the mean than data sets with a high MAD.

The MAD can be found by using the formula $\mathbf{MAD} = \dfrac{|x_1 - \bar{x}| + |x_2 - \bar{x}| + \cdots + |x_n - \bar{x}|}{n}$, where $x_1, x_2, \ldots, x_n$ are the data values, $\bar{x}$ is the mean, and n is the number of data values.

Activity

The table shows the numbers of hours worked by two students at part-time jobs over the past 5 weeks.

Hours Spent Working					
Student A	15	20	15	25	20
Student B	10	25	20	30	25

1. Find the mean of each data set.

2. For each data set, subtract the mean from each data value. Then find the absolute value of the difference. Complete the tables.

Student A	
x_i	$\lvert x_i - \bar{x} \rvert$
15	
20	
15	
25	
20	

Student B	
x_i	$\lvert x_i - \bar{x} \rvert$
10	
25	
20	
30	
25	

3. For each data set, find the mean of the absolute values of the differences you found in Exercise 2. This is the mean absolute deviation.

© 4. **Writing** Compare the numbers of hours worked by each student. Use the mean absolute deviation in your comparison.

Exercises

Find the mean absolute deviation of each data set. Then compare the data sets.

5.

Average Wait Times (minutes)								
Diner A	11	19	16	8	10	15	13	16
Diner B	5	22	14	13	18	7	9	12

6.

Digital Camera Prices										
Store A	$85	$110	$79	$184	$125	$35	$179	$104	$140	$75
Store B	$49	$35	$122	$65	$110	$80	$52	$96	$77	$115

LESSON LAB

Use With Lesson 6-2

Standard Deviation

MCC9-12.S.ID.2 Use statistics appropriate to the shape of the data distribution to compare . . . spread . . . of two or more different data sets.

Statisticians use measures of dispersion to describe how spread out the values in a data set are. One measure of dispersion is *standard deviation*. **Standard deviation** is a measure of how the values in a data set vary, or deviate, from the mean.

Statisticians use several special symbols in the formula for standard deviation.

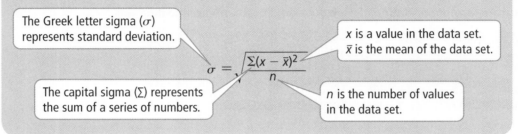

The Greek letter sigma (σ) represents standard deviation.

x is a value in the data set.
$\bar{x}$ is the mean of the data set.

$$\sigma = \sqrt{\frac{\Sigma(x - \bar{x})^2}{n}}$$

The capital sigma (Σ) represents the sum of a series of numbers.

n is the number of values in the data set.

Example

Find the mean and standard deviation of each data set. Which data set has greater standard deviation?

Step 1 Find the mean, $\bar{x}$.

Step 2 Find the difference between each data value and the mean, $x - \bar{x}$.

Step 3 Square each difference, $(x - \bar{x})^2$.

Step 4 Find the average (mean) of these squares, $\frac{\Sigma(x - \bar{x})^2}{n}$.

Step 5 Take the square root to find the standard deviation, $\sqrt{\frac{\Sigma(x - \bar{x})^2}{n}}$.

Data Set 1			
x_1	$\bar{x}_1$	$x_1 - \bar{x}_1$	$(x_1 - \bar{x}_1)^2$
12.6	15	−2.4	5.76
15.1	15	0.1	0.01
11.2	15	−3.8	14.44
17.9	15	2.9	8.41
18.2	15	3.2	10.24
$\frac{\Sigma(x_1 - \bar{x}_1)^2}{n}$			7.772
$\sqrt{\frac{\Sigma(x_1 - \bar{x}_1)^2}{n}}$			≈ 2.79

Data Set 2			
x_2	$\bar{x}_2$	$x_2 - \bar{x}_2$	$(x_2 - \bar{x}_2)^2$
13.4	14.5	−1.1	1.21
11.7	14.5	−2.8	7.84
18.3	14.5	3.8	14.44
14.8	14.5	0.3	0.09
14.3	14.5	−0.2	0.04
$\frac{\Sigma(x_2 - \bar{x}_2)^2}{n}$			4.724
$\sqrt{\frac{\Sigma(x_2 - \bar{x}_2)^2}{n}}$			≈ 2.17

Data set 1 has a greater standard deviation at 2.79.

Exercises

Find the mean and standard deviation of each data set. Round to the nearest hundredth. Which data set has the greater standard deviation?

1. Data set 1: 4, 8, 5, 12, 3, 9, 5, 2

Data set 2: 5, 9, 11, 4, 6, 11, 2, 7

2. Data set 1: 102, 98, 103, 86, 101, 110

Data set 2: 90, 89, 100, 97, 102, 97

3. Data set 1: 8.2, 11.6, 8.7, 10.6, 9.4, 10.1, 9.3

Data set 2: 9.3, 10.2, 8.1, 12.3, 8.7, 9.9, 10.1

4. Data set 1: 32, 40, 35, 28, 42, 32, 44

Data set 2: 40, 38, 51, 39, 46, 40, 52

MCC9-12.S.ID.2 Use statistics appropriate to the shape of the data distribution to compare center . . . and spread . . . of two or more different data sets. Also **MCC9-12.N.Q.1, MCC9-12.S.ID.1**

Objectives To make and interpret box-and-whisker plots
To find quartiles and percentiles

 Solve It! Write your solution to the Solve It in the space below.

In the Solve It, you may have looked at different parts of each data set in order to compare the two data sets.

Essential Understanding Separating data into subsets is a useful way to summarize and compare data sets.

Quartiles are values that divide a data set into four equal parts. The median (or second quartile, Q_2) separates the data into upper and lower halves. The first quartile (Q_1) is the median of the lower half of the data. The third quartile (Q_3) is the median of the upper half of the data. The **interquartile range** is the difference between the third and first quartiles.

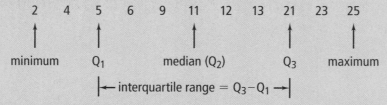

For a set of data that has an odd number of values, you do not include the median in either half when finding the first and third quartiles.

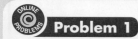 **Problem 1** **Summarizing a Data Set**

Got It? What are the minimum, first quartile, median, third quartile, and maximum of each data set?

a. 95 85 75 85 65 60 100 105 75 85 75

b. 11 19 7 5 21 53

 Practice Find the minimum, first quartile, median, third quartile, and maximum of each data set.

1. 4.5 3.2 6.3 5.2 5 4.8 6 3.9 12

2. 55 53 67 52 50 49 51 52 52

> **Think**
>
> How do you arrange the given data to find the required values?

A **box-and-whisker plot** is a graph that summarizes a set of data by displaying it along a number line. It consists of three parts: a box and two whiskers.

Box-and-Whisker Plot

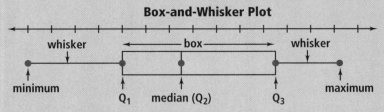

- The left whisker extends from the minimum to the first quartile. It represents about 25% of the data.
- The box extends from the first quartile to the third quartile and has a vertical line through the median. The length of the box represents the interquartile range. It contains about 50% of the data.
- The right whisker extends from the third quartile to the maximum. It represents about 25% of the data.

 **Problem 2** Making a Box-and-Whisker Plot

Got It? What box-and-whisker plot represents the following monthly sales, in millions of dollars, of audio devices: 15   4   9   16   10   16   8   14   25   34?

Ⓐ **Practice** Make a box-and-whisker plot to represent each set of data.

3. weekly museum visitors: 531   469   573   206   374   421   505   489   702

4. camera prices: $280 $220 $224 $70 $410 $90 $30 $120

Problem 3 Interpreting Box-and-Whisker Plots

Got It? Use the box-and-whisker plots from Problem 3. What do the medians tell you about the average monthly rainfalls for Miami and New Orleans?

Practice 5. **Fuel Use** Use the box-and-whisker plots below. What do they tell you about the fuel efficiency for each type of vehicle? Explain.

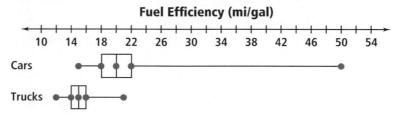

Percentiles separate data sets into 100 equal parts. The **percentile rank** of a data value is the percentage of data values that are less than or equal to that value.

Problem 4 Finding a Percentile Rank

Got It? a. Of the 25 scores in Problem 4, there are 15 scores less than or equal to 85. What is the percentile rank of 85?

> **Think**
> **How can you write a proportion to solve this problem?**

© b. **Reasoning** Is it possible to have a percentile rank of 0? Explain.

Practice

6. Of 10 test scores, six are less than or equal to 80. What is the percentile rank of a test score of 80?

7. Of 35 judges' scores awarded during a gymnastics event, 28 are less than or equal to 7.5. What is the percentile rank of a score of 7.5?

 ## Lesson Check

Do you know HOW?

Identify the minimum, first quartile, median, third quartile, and maximum of each data set. Then make a box-and-whisker plot of each data set.

8. file sizes (megabytes): 54 100 84 124 188 48 256

9. daily attendance: 29 24 28 32 30 31 26 33

10. In the box-and-whisker plots at the right, which class has the greater interquartile range of arm spans?

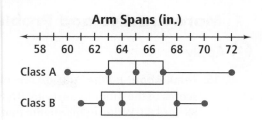

Arm Spans (in.)

Do you UNDERSTAND?

MATHEMATICAL PRACTICES

11. Vocabulary Which portion of a box-and-whisker plot represents the interquartile range?

12. Students taking a make-up test receive the following grades: 77, 89, 88, 67, 91, 95, 83, 79, 81, and 65. Which grade has a percentile rank of 70?

13. Reasoning About what percent of the data in a data set falls between the minimum value and the third quartile? Explain.

14. Error Analysis A test is graded on a scale from 0 to 100. Your friend says that if you score a 78, your percentile rank must be 78. Is your friend correct? Explain.

More Practice and Problem-Solving Exercises

B Apply

15. Think About a Plan You are one of the finalists at a science fair. The scores of the other finalists are 87, 89, 81, 85, 87, 83, 86, 94, 90, 97, 80, 89, 85, and 88. Write an inequality that represents your possible scores if your percentile rank is 80.
  - What percent of the scores must be less than or equal to your score?
  - What is the total number of finalists' scores?

16. Writing Explain the difference between *range* and *interquartile range*.

17. Basketball The heights of the players on a basketball team are 74 in., 79 in., 71.5 in., 81 in., 73 in., 76 in., 78 in., 71 in., 72 in., and 73.5 in. When the 76-in.-tall player is replaced, the percentile rank of the 73.5-in.-tall player becomes 60. Write an inequality that represents the possible heights of the replacement player.

18. Open-Ended Make a data set of 10 numbers that has a median of 22, an interquartile range of 10, and a minimum less than 4.

19. Reasoning Must the third quartile of a data set be less than the maximum value? Explain.

STEM 20. Packaging A cereal company is choosing between two devices to package their cereal into bags. The box-and-whisker plots at the right show the weights of the bags packed by each device.
  a. Which device produces packages with a more consistent weight? Explain.
  b. Which device should be chosen if the manufacturer wants to minimize the number of packages with weights less than 17 oz? More than 17.2 oz? Explain.

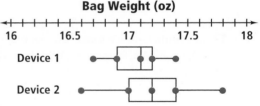

C Challenge

21. Reasoning Can you find the mean, median, and mode of a data set by looking at a box-and-whisker plot? Explain.

22. Of 100 people that take a test, nine have scores greater than 93. What is the percentile rank of a score of 93?

6-4 | Scatter Plots and Trend Lines

MCC9-12.S.ID.6.c Fit a linear function for a scatter plot . . . Also MCC9-12.S.ID.6, MCC9-12.S.ID.6.a, MCC9-12.S.ID.7, MCC9-12.S.ID.8, MCC9-12.S.ID.9

Objectives To write an equation of a trend line and of a line of best fit
To use a trend line and a line of best fit to make predictions

Solve It! Write your solution to the Solve It in the space below.

In the Solve It, the number of albums downloaded per year and the number of CDs sold per year are related.

Essential Understanding You can determine whether two sets of numerical data are related by graphing them as ordered pairs. If the two sets of data are related, you may be able to use a line to estimate or predict values.

A **scatter plot** is a graph that relates two different sets of data by displaying them as ordered pairs. Most scatter plots are in the first quadrant of the coordinate plane because the data are usually positive numbers.

You can use scatter plots to find trends in data. The scatter plots below show the three types of relationships that two sets of data may have.

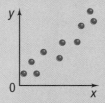

When *y* tends to increase as *x* increases, the two sets of data have a **positive correlation**.

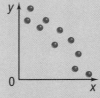

When *y* tends to decrease as *x* increases, the two sets of data have a **negative correlation**.

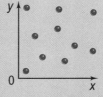

When *x* and *y* are not related, the two sets of data have **no correlation**.

 **Problem 1** **Making a Scatter Plot and Describing Its Correlation**

Got It?

a. Make a scatter plot of the data in the table below. What type of relationship does the scatter plot show?

Gasoline Purchases							
Dollars Spent	10	11	9	10	13	5	8	4
Gallons Bought	2.5	2.8	2.3	2.6	3.3	1.3	2.2	1.1

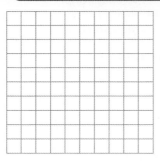

b. Reasoning Consider the population of a city and the number of letters in the name of the city. Would you expect a *positive correlation,* a *negative correlation,* or *no correlation* between the two sets of data? Explain your reasoning.

A **Practice** For each table in Exercises 1 and 2, make a scatter plot of the data.
Describe the type of correlation the scatter plot shows.

1.

Jeans Sales				
Average Price ($)	21	28	36	40
Number Sold	130	112	82	65

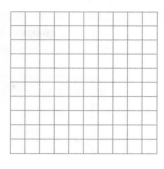

2.

Gasoline Purchases					
Dollars Spent	10	11	9	8	13
Gallons Bought	2.6	3	2.4	2.2	3.5

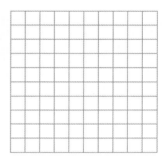

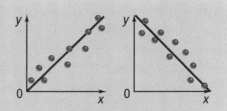

When two sets of data have a positive or negative correlation, you can use a *trend line* to show the correlation more clearly. A **trend line** is a line on a scatter plot, drawn near the points, that shows a correlation.

You can use a trend line to estimate a value between two known data values or to predict a value outside the range of known data values. **Interpolation** is estimating a value between two known values. **Extrapolation** is predicting a value outside the range of known values.

Problem 2   **Writing an Equation of a Trend Line**

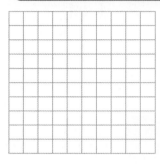

Plan

How do you draw an accurate trend line?

Got It?   **a.** Make a scatter plot of the data below. Draw a trend line and write its equation. What is the approximate body length of a 7-month-old panda?

Body Length of a Panda								
Age (month)	1	2	3	4	5	6	8	9
Body Length (in.)	8.0	11.75	15.5	16.7	20.1	22.2	26.5	29.0

b. Reasoning Do you think you can use your model to extrapolate the body length of a 3-year-old panda? Explain.

Practice

Theme Parks Use the table below for Exercises 3 and 4.

Attendance and Revenue at U.S. Theme Parks									
Year	1990	1992	1994	1996	1998	2000	2002	2004	2006
Attendance (millions)	253	267	267	290	300	317	324	328	335
Revenue (billions of dollars)	5.7	6.5	7.0	7.9	8.7	9.6	9.9	10.8	11.5

Source: International Association of Amusement Parks and Attractions

3. Make a scatter plot of the data pairs (year, attendance). Draw a trend line and write its equation. Estimate the attendance at U.S. theme parks in 2005.

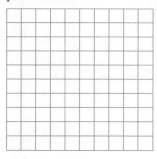

4. Make a scatter plot of the data pairs (year, revenue). Draw a trend line and write its equation. Predict the revenue at U.S. theme parks in 2012.

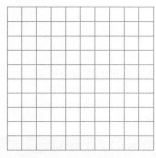

The trend line that shows the relationship between two sets of data most accurately is called the **line of best fit**. A graphing calculator computes the equation of the line of best fit using a method called linear regression.

The graphing calculator also gives you the **correlation coefficient** r, a number from -1 to 1, that tells you how closely the equation models the data.

$$r = -1 \qquad r = 0 \qquad r = 1$$

strong negative correlation   no correlation   strong positive correlation

The nearer r is to 1 or -1, the more closely the data cluster around the line of best fit. If r is near 1, the data lie close to a line of best fit with positive slope. If r is near -1, the data lie close to a line of best fit with negative slope.

Problem 3   Finding the Line of Best Fit

Got It?   **a.** Use the data in Problem 3. Predict the cost of attending in the 2016–2017 academic year.

b. Reasoning What does the slope of the line of best fit in Problem 3 tell you about the rate of change in the cost?

A Practice   **5. Entertainment** Use a graphing calculator to find the equation of the line of best fit for the data in the table. Find the value of the correlation coefficient r to three decimal places. Then predict the number of movie tickets sold in the U.S. in 2014.

Movie Tickets Sold in U.S. by Year										
Year	1998	1999	2000	2001	2002	2003	2004	2005	2006	2007
Tickets Sold (millions)	1289	1311	1340	1339	1406	1421	1470	1415	1472	1470

SOURCE: Motion Picture Association of America

Causation is when a change in one quantity causes a change in a second quantity. A correlation between quantities does not always imply causation.

Problem 4 Identifying Whether Relationships Are Causal

Got It? In the following situations, is there likely to be a correlation? If so, does the correlation reflect a causal relationship? Explain.

a. the cost of a family's vacation and the size of their house

b. the time spent exercising and the number of Calories burned

Practice In each situation, tell whether a correlation is likely. If it is, tell whether the correlation reflects a causal relationship. Explain your reasoning.

6. the amount of time you study for a test and the score you receive

7. a person's height and the number of letters in the person's name

You have used a graphing calculator to find lines of best fit for linear data. However, sometimes a scatter plot suggests a nonlinear trend for a data set. You can also use a graphing calculator to determine exponential models for nonlinear data.

 Problem 5 **Analyzing a Nonlinear Trend**

 Think

How can a scatter plot show whether a linear or exponential model is better?

Got It? The table shows the value of Denise's car each year since she purchased it. Use a graphing calculator to make a scatter plot for the data. Which is a suitable model for the data, a linear model or an exponential model? Write the model and predict the value of Denise's car after 8 years.

Value of Denise's Car					
Age (years), x	1	2	3	4	5
Value (thousands of dollars), y	28.6	18.5	14.1	10.2	8.9

 Practice **8.** The table shows the values of a stock during the first several months after the stock was bought. Use a graphing calculator to make a scatter plot for the data. Which is a suitable model for the data, a linear model or an exponential model? Write the model and predict the value of the stock after 10 months.

Values of a Stock Over Time						
Months, x	1	2	3	4	5	6
Stock Value (in dollars), y	4.10	5.40	7.30	9.93	13.51	17.90

9. The table shows the number of bacteria in a culture at the start of each hour as it is being studied. Use a graphing calculator to make a scatter plot for the data. Which is a suitable model for the data, a linear model or an exponential model? Write the model and predict the number of bacteria after 12 hours.

Bacteria Culture 0819023								
Number of Hours, *x*	1	2	3	4	5	6	7	8
Number of Bacteria, *y*	1200	780	510	330	210	140	100	85

Lesson Check

Do you know HOW?

Use the table for Exercises 10–12.

10. Make a scatter plot of the data. What type of relationship does the scatter plot show?

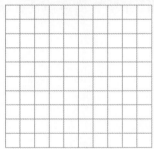

Average Maximum Daily Temperature in January for Northern Latitudes							
Latitude (°N)	35	33	30	25	43	40	39
Temperature (°F)	46	52	67	76	32	37	44

11. Draw a trend line on the scatter plot and write its equation.

12. Predict the average maximum daily temperature in January at a latitude of 50° N.

Do you UNDERSTAND?

13. Vocabulary Given a set of data pairs, how would you decide whether to use interpolation or extrapolation to find a certain value?

14. Compare and Contrast How are a trend line and the line of best fit for a set of data pairs similar? How are they different?

15. Error Analysis Refer to the table at the right. A student says that the data have a negative correlation because as x decreases, y also decreases. What is the student's error?

x	10	7	5	4	1	0
y	1	0	−2	−4	−7	−9

More Practice and Problem-Solving Exercises

B Apply

16. Writing Give two data sets that are correlated but do *not* have a causal relationship.

17. Business During one month at a local deli, the amount of ham sold decreased as the amount of turkey sold increased. Is this an example of *positive correlation*, *negative correlation*, or *no correlation*?

18. Think About a Plan Students measured the diameters and circumferences of the tops of a variety of cylinders. Below are the data that they collected. Estimate the diameter of a cylinder with circumference 22 cm.

Cylinder Tops										
Diameter (cm)	3	3	5	6	8	8	9.5	10	10	12
Circumference (cm)	9.3	9.5	16	18.8	25	25.6	29.5	31.5	30.9	39.5

- How can you use a scatter plot to find an equation of a trend line?
- How can you use the equation of the trend line to make an estimate?

19. The table represents the population of Covetown at different times since it was founded in 1980.

Population of Covetown						
Year	1980	1990	2000	2005	2010	2012
Population	8400	17,300	35,900	51,100	73,500	85,200

   a. Let x represent the number of years since 1980 so that $x = 0$ represents 1980. Let y represent the population of Covetown in thousands of people. Using these definitions, rewrite the values in the table. Explain why doing so will make it easier to find a best-fitting model for the data.
   b. Make a scatter plot of the data. Do the data appear to be linear or exponential?
   c. Write an equation of the best-fitting line or best-fitting curve. What is the correlation coefficient? Does your equation appear to be a good fit for the data set?
   d. According to your equation, what was the population of Covetown in 1995 and what will the population be in 2025? Which estimate do you think is likely to be more accurate? Explain.

20. U.S. Population Use the data below.

Estimated Population of the United States (thousands)							
Year	2000	2001	2002	2003	2004	2005	2006
Male	138,482	140,079	141,592	142,937	144,467	145,973	147,512
Female	143,734	145,147	146,533	147,858	149,170	150,533	151,886

Source: U.S. Census Bureau

   a. Make a scatter plot of the data pairs (male population, female population).
   b. Draw a trend line and write its equation.
   c. Use your equation to predict the U.S. female population if the U.S. male population increases to 150,000,000.
   d. Reasoning Consider a scatter plot of the data pairs (year, male population). Would it be reasonable to use this scatter plot to predict the U.S. male population in 2035? Explain your reasoning.

21. **a.** **Graphing Calculator** Use a graphing calculator to find the equation of the line of best fit for the data below. Let $x = 8$ represent 1998, $x = 9$ represent 1999, and so on.

U.S. Computer and Video Game Unit Sales									
Year	1998	1999	2000	2001	2002	2003	2004	2005	2006	2007
Unit Sales (millions)	152.4	184.5	196.3	210.3	225.8	240.9	249.5	229.5	241.6	267.9

SOURCE: The NPD Group/Retail Tracking Service

b. What is the slope of the line of best fit? What does the slope mean in terms of the number of computer and video game units sold?

c. What is the y-intercept of the line of best fit? What does the y-intercept mean in terms of the number of computer and video game units sold?

Ⓒ Challenge

Ⓔ **22.** **a.** Make a scatter plot of the data below. Then find the equation of the line of best fit. Draw the line of best fit on your scatter plot.

Car Stopping Distances								
Speed (mi/h)	10	15	20	25	30	35	40	45
Stopping Distance (ft)	27	44	63	85	109	136	164	196

b. Use your equation to predict the stopping distance at 90 mi/h.

c. **Reasoning** The actual stopping distance at 90 mi/h is close to 584 ft. Why do you think this distance is not close to your prediction?

d. Suppose you plot (90, 584) on your scatter plot. What effect would it have on the slope and y-intercept of the line of best fit you found in part (a)?

ACTIVITY LAB

Use With Lesson 6-4

Using Residuals

MCC9-12.S.ID.6.b ... Assess the fit of a function by ... analyzing residuals.

In Lesson 6-4, you learned how to assess the line of best fit by using the correlation coefficient r. In this activity you will learn how to determine whether the best linear function is a good fit for the data. As you learn different types of functions in future chapters, residual plots will help you analyze the fit of other models.

A **residual** is the difference between the y-value of a data point and the corresponding y-value of a model for the data set.

You can find a residual by calculating $y - \hat{y}$, where y represents the y-value of the data set and $\hat{y}$ represents the corresponding y-value predicted from the model.

Activity

The linear function $\hat{y} = 2.3x + 33.4$ models the data shown below.

Mean Heights of Boys Ages 5 to 13

Age (yr)	5	6	7	8	9	10	11	12	13
Height (in.)	44.5	46.9	49.7	52.2	54.4	55.7	58.5	60.9	63.1

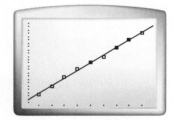

1. Complete the table below to calculate the residuals.

Age (x)	Height (y)	Predicted value $\hat{y} = 2.3x + 33.4$	Residual $y - \hat{y}$
5	44.5	2.3(5) + 33.4 = 44.9	44.5 − 44.9 = −0.4
6			
7			
8			
9			
10			
11			
12			
13			

You can plot each of the points $(x, y - \hat{y})$ on a coordinate plane, and analyze the residual plot to assess whether the function is a good fit for the data. For a good fit, the points appear to have no pattern.

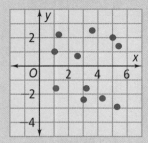

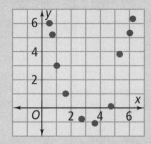

There is no apparent pattern in the residual plot. This indicates that the model function is a good fit for the data.

The points in the residual plot form a pattern. This indicates that the model function is not a good fit for the data.

2. Plot the points $(x, y - \hat{y})$ from the table in Exercise 1 on a coordinate plane.

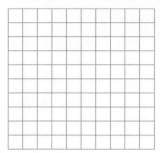

3. Do the points appear to form a pattern?

Ⓖ 4. **Writing** Explain how you can use the residual plot to determine whether the model function is a good fit for the data.

Exercises

5. You model two data sets using linear models. The resulting residual plots are shown at the right. Which residual plot indicates that the linear model is a good fit for the data? Justify your answer.

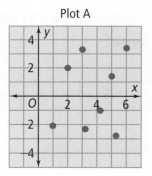

Plot A

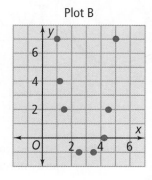

Plot B

6. Use a graphing calculator to determine the line of best fit for the data set below. Then use a residual plot to determine whether the line of best fit is a good model. Explain.

Latitude and Temperature in Selected Cities

City	Latitude (°N)	Mean High Temperature in April (°F)
Lagos, Nigeria	6	89
San Juan, Puerto Rico	18	84
Kolkata, India	23	97
Cairo, Egypt	30	83
Tokyo, Japan	35	63
Rome, Italy	42	68
Belgrade, Serbia	45	45
London, England	52	56
Copenhagen, Denmark	56	50
Moscow, Russia	56	47

6-5 Two-Way Frequency Tables

MCC9-12.S.ID.5 Summarize categorical data for two categories in two-way frequency tables. Interpret relative frequencies in the context of the data . . . Recognize possible associations and trends in the data.

Objective   To use two-way frequency tables to summarize, interpret, and analyze trends in data

 Solve It!   Write your solution to the Solve It in the space below.

In the Solve It, you used a *two-way frequency* table to draw a conclusion about categorical data. Categorical data are data that fall into categories, such as boy or girl. A **two-way frequency table** is a table in which frequencies correspond to two variables. One variable is used to categorize rows, and a second variable is used to categorize columns. Two-way frequency tables have at least two rows and two columns. An entry in the body of the table is a **joint frequency**. An entry in the Total row or Total column is a **marginal frequency**.

Bicycle Status			
Gender	Own a Bicycle	Do Not Own a Bicycle	Total
Boys	16	4	20
Girls	18	12	30
Total	34	16	50

grand total

joint frequency

Essential Understanding Two-way frequency tables are a convenient way to show categorical data. You can use two-way frequency tables to analyze categorical data.

Problem 1   Making a Two-Way Frequency Table

Think

How can you check if your table is reasonable?

Got It?   A survey asked 170 freshmen and sophomores whether they preferred Math or English. Of the 87 freshmen, 36 said that they preferred Math. Of the 83 sophomores, 27 said that they preferred English. Make a two-way frequency table for the data.

Ⓐ Practice

1. **News** A survey asked 295 males and females whether they preferred reading about the news from a newspaper or on the Internet. Of the 138 males, 97 said that they preferred the Internet. Of the 157 females, 32 said that they preferred a newspaper. Make a two-way frequency table for the data.

2. **Foreign Language** A survey asked 152 juniors and seniors whether they preferred Spanish or French. Of the 68 juniors, 34 said that they preferred Spanish. Of the 84 seniors, 47 said that they preferred Spanish. Make a two-way frequency table for the data.

The **relative frequency** of a category, such as girls who own a bicycle, is the ratio of the frequency of the category to the total frequency. So the relative frequency of girls who own a bicycle in the Solve It is $\frac{18}{30} = 0.6$.

You find a **joint relative frequency** by dividing a frequency that is not in the Total row or the Total column by the grand total.

You find a **marginal relative frequency** by dividing a row total or a column total by the grand total.

A **two-way relative frequency table** displays both joint relative frequencies and marginal relative frequencies.

Bicycle Status			
Gender	Own a Bicycle	Do Not Own a Bicycle	Total
Boys	$\frac{16}{50} = 0.32$	$\frac{4}{50} = 0.08$	$\frac{20}{50} = 0.4$
Girls	$\frac{18}{50} = 0.36$	$\frac{12}{50} = 0.24$	$\frac{30}{50} = 0.6$
Total	$\frac{34}{50} = 0.68$	$\frac{16}{50} = 0.32$	$\frac{50}{50} = 1$

marginal relative frequency

joint relative frequency

Problem 2   **Making and Interpreting a Two-Way Relative Frequency Table**

Got It?   Use the table in Problem 2.

   a. What is the joint relative frequency of women who saw Movie B?

   b. What is the marginal relative frequency of people who saw Movie A?

3. Use the data from Exercise 1.

    a. Make a two-way relative frequency table for the data.

    b. What is the joint relative frequency of females who preferred the Internet?

    c. What is the marginal relative frequency of people who preferred a newspaper?

4. Use the data from Exercise 2.

    a. Make a two-way relative frequency table for the data.

    b. What is the joint relative frequency of juniors who preferred French?

    c. What is the marginal relative frequency of seniors?

You can find **conditional relative frequency** by dividing a joint frequency by that frequency's row total or column total.

Problem 3 **Calculating Conditional Relative Frequency**

Got It? Use the table in Problem 3. Round to the nearest hundredth.

> **Think**
>
> **How do you calculate conditional relative frequency?**

a. What is the conditional relative frequency that a person surveyed opposed the bond issue, given that the person was between 18 and 25?

b. What is the conditional relative frequency that a person surveyed opposed the bond issue, given that the person was between 26 and 64?

c. What is the conditional relative frequency that a person surveyed opposed the bond issue, given that the person was 65 or older?

ⓒd. Reasoning What conclusion can you draw based on the conditional relative frequencies you found in parts (a)–(c)?

Practice 5. **Baseball** The table shows statistics about a baseball team and the number of times players reached base for different positions in the batting order.

	Position in Lineup		
	1–3	4–6	7–9
Reach Base	9	6	2
Out	3	4	7

    a. What is the conditional relative frequency that a player batting in the 1st, 2nd, or 3rd position reached base?

    b. What is the conditional relative frequency that a player batting in the 4th, 5th, or 6th position reached base?

    c. What is the conditional relative frequency that a player batting in the 7th, 8th, or 9th position reached base?

6. **Surveys** The table shows the results of a survey about 8th grade boys and girls and the number of times they packed their lunch each week.

Number of Times Packing Lunch Each Week		
Gender	0–2	3–5
Boy	23	89
Girl	62	71

a. What is the conditional relative frequency that a person surveyed packed a lunch 0–2 times each week, given that the person was a boy?

b. What is the conditional relative frequency that a person surveyed packed a lunch 0–2 times each week, given that the person was a girl?

©c. **Reasoning** What conclusion can you draw based on the conditional relative frequencies you found in parts (a)–(b)?

Lesson Check

Do you know HOW?

The table shows the numbers of freshman boys and girls who play and do not play a sport.

Sport Status			
Gender	Play a Sport	Do Not Play a Sport	Total
Boy	58	62	120
Girl	26	94	120
Total	84	156	240

7. What is the marginal frequency of freshmen who played a sport?

8. What is the marginal frequency of freshmen who were girls?

9. What is the joint relative frequency of the girls who played a sport?

10. What is the joint relative frequency of the boys who did not play a sport?

Do you UNDERSTAND?

11. Vocabulary Which type of frequency is found by dividing a joint frequency by that frequency's row total or column total?

12. Compare and Contrast What is the difference between joint frequency and marginal frequency?

13. Writing How can you make a two-way relative frequency table from a two-way frequency table?

14. Reasoning Explain why the grand total of a two-way relative frequency table is always equal to 1.

More Practice and Problem-Solving Exercises

MATHEMATICAL
PRACTICES

B Apply

ⓒ 15. Think About a Plan A survey asked 615 males and females whether they had a television in their bedroom. Of the 375 males, 298 said they had a television in their bedroom. Of the 240 females, 162 said they did not have a television in their bedroom. What is the joint relative frequency of females who had a television in their bedroom? What is the marginal relative frequency of people who did not have a television in their bedroom?
- How can you show the information?
- How can you find the missing information?
- How do you find the joint relative frequencies and marginal relative frequencies?

16. Text Message Plans A survey asked 1,162 males and females whether they had a 500 text messages per month plan or an unlimited text message plan. Of the 541 females, 108 said they had a 500 text messages per month plan. There were 196 people who said they had a 500 text messages per month plan. What is the joint relative frequency of males who had an unlimited text message plan? What is the marginal relative frequency of people who had an unlimited text message plan?

ⓒ 17. Writing Use the information from Exercise 16. Explain how to find the conditional relative frequency that a person surveyed was a female, given they had an unlimited text message plan.

ⓒ 18. Error Analysis Your friend surveyed people about their hair color. Of the 315 males, 75 had black hair, 130 had brown hair, and 12 had red hair. Of the 509 females, 286 had brown hair and 151 had blond hair. There were 122 males and females that had black hair. Your friend made the two-way frequency table below. Describe and correct his error.

Hair Color					
Gender	Black	Brown	Blond	Red	Total
Male	75	130	98	12	315
Female	47	286	151	22	509
Total	122	416	249	34	824

19. **Movies** McKenzie surveyed 800 students and adults who attended two different movies, one shown at 7:00 and one shown at 9:00. There was a total of 465 adults that attended either the 7:00 movie or the 9:00 movie. Of the 330 people that went to the 7:00 movie, 120 were adults.
    a. Make a two-way frequency table.
    b. What is the conditional relative frequency that a person surveyed was a student, given that the person went to the 9:00 movie?
    c. What is the conditional relative frequency that a person surveyed was an adult, given that the person went to the 9:00 movie?
    d. **Reasoning** What conclusion can you draw based on the conditional relative frequencies you found in parts (b)–(c)?

20. **Reasoning** Explain how to draw a conclusion based on conditional relative frequencies.

Challenge

21. **Shirt Color** A survey asked 16 boys and 14 girls about their shirt color. There were 8 boys with a blue shirt, 6 girls with a red shirt, and 6 girls with a white shirt. There were a total of 9 boys and girls with a red shirt.
    a. Make a two-way frequency table.
    b. Make a two-way relative frequency table.
    c. What is the joint relative frequency of a boy wearing a red shirt?
    d. What is the joint relative frequency of a girl wearing a blue shirt?
    e. What is the marginal relative frequency of a person wearing a white shirt?
    f. What is the conditional relative frequency that a person surveyed was a boy, given that the person wore a blue shirt? Red shirt? White shirt?
    g. **Reasoning** What conclusions can you draw based on the conditional relative frequencies you found in part (f)?

6 Chapter Review

6-1 Frequency and Histograms

Quick Review

A **histogram** displays data in intervals, showing the frequency of values in each interval.

Example

Below are the prices of the television models sold at an electronics store. What is a histogram of the data?

$1399 $1349 $999 $2149 $149 $279
$449 $379 $1379 $799 $3199 $1099
$499 $899 $949 $1799 $1699 $3499

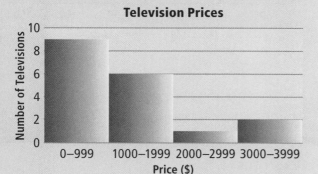

Exercises

Use the data to make a histogram.

1. customers: 141 128 132 141 152 169 121 133 131 156 142 136 135 144 135 153

2. workout times (min): 41 29 46 39 37 44 33 51 42 30

Tell whether each histogram is *uniform*, *symmetric*, or *skewed*.

3.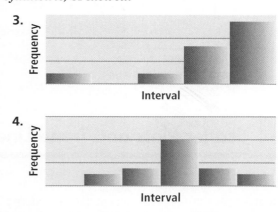

4.

6-2 Measures of Central Tendency and Dispersion

Quick Review

The **mean** of a data set equals $\frac{\text{sum of the data values}}{\text{total number of data values}}$. The **median** is the middle value in the data set when the values are arranged in order. The **mode** is the data item that occurs the most times.

Example

What are the mean, median, and mode of the data?

5.6, 7.9, 7.0, 5.9, 7.8, 6.2, 6.4, 5.2, and 5.6

mean:

$$\frac{5.6 + 7.9 + 7.0 + 5.9 + 7.8 + 6.2 + 6.4 + 5.2 + 5.6}{9} = 6.4$$

5.2 5.6 5.6 5.9 6.2 6.4 7.0 7.8 7.9   Order the data.

median: 6.2   6.2 is the middle value.

mode: 5.6   5.6 occurs most often.

Exercises

5. Find the mean, median, mode, and range of the points scored by a football team.: 23 31 26 27 25 28 23 23 25 29 29 29 25 22 30

6. **Cats** A veterinarian examines 9 cats. The weights of the cats are 13.4 lb, 13.1 lb, 10.4 lb, 6.8 lb, 11.4 lb, 10.8 lb, 13.4 lb, 11.3 lb, and 9.3 lb. Find the mean, median, and mode of the data. Which measure of central tendency best describes the data?

7. **Basketball** A basketball player scores 22, 19, 25, and 17 points in four games. How many points does the basketball player need to score in the fifth game to average 22 points scored per game?

6-3 Box-and-Whisker Plots

Quick Review

A **box-and-whisker plot** organizes data values into four groups using the minimum value, the first quartile, the median, the third quartile, and the maximum value.

Example

What box-and-whisker plot represents the test scores below?

62 57 78 69 85 43 94 82 61 90 83 51 67 88 55

Arrange the data in order from least to greatest.

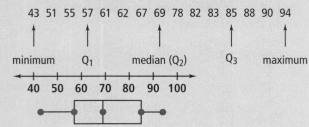

43 51 55 57 61 62 67 69 78 82 83 85 88 90 94

minimum Q_1 median (Q_2) Q_3 maximum

40 50 60 70 80 90 100

Exercises

Make a box-and-whisker plot of each data set.

8. movie lengths (min):

   125 117 174 131 142 108 188 162 155 167 129 133 147 175 150

9. dog weights (lb):

   23 15 88 34 33 49 52 67 42 71 28

10. book lengths (pages):

   178 223 198 376 284 156 245 202 315 266

11. Which box-and-whisker plot represents the data set with the greater interquartile range? Explain.

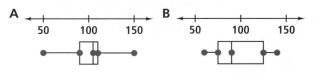

A
50   100   150

B
50   100   150

6-4 Scatter Plots and Trend Lines

Quick Review

A **scatter plot** displays two sets of data as ordered pairs. A **trend line** for a scatter plot shows the correlation between the two sets of data. The most accurate trend line is the **line of best fit**. To estimate or predict values on a scatter plot, you can use **interpolation** or **extrapolation**.

Example

Estimate the length of the kudzu vine in Week 3.

When $w = 3$, $\ell \approx 10$. So in Week 3, the length of the kudzu vine was about 10 ft.

Predict the length of the kudzu vine in Week 11.

$\ell = 3.5w$ Use the equation of the trend line.

$\ell = 3.5(11)$ Substitute 11 for w.

$\ell = 38.5$ Simplify.

The length of the vine in Week 11 will be about 38.5 ft.

Kudzu Vine Growth

Length (ft), ℓ

$\ell = 3.5w$

Week, w

Exercises

12. a. Make a scatter plot of the data below.

Heights and Arm Spans						
Height (m)	1.5	1.8	1.7	2.0	1.7	2.1
Arm Span (m)	1.4	1.7	1.7	1.9	1.6	2.0

b. Write an equation of a reasonable trend line or use a graphing calculator to find the equation of the line of best fit.

c. Estimate the arm span of someone who is 1.6 m tall.

d. Predict the arm span of someone who is 2.2 m tall.

6-5 Two-Way Frequency Tables

Quick Review

A **two-way frequency table** is a table in which frequencies correspond to two variables. An entry in the body of a table is a **joint frequency**. An entry in the Total row or Total column is a **marginal frequency**. The **relative frequency** of a category is the ratio of the frequency of the category to the total frequency.

You find a **joint relative frequency** by dividing a frequency that is not in the Total row or Total column by the grand total. You find a **marginal relative frequency** by dividing a row total or a column total by the grand total. A **two-way relative frequency table** displays both joint and marginal relative frequencies.

You can find **conditional relative frequency** by dividing a joint frequency by that frequency's row or column total.

Example

What is the joint relative frequency of boys whose favorite sport is basketball?

	Favorite Sport		
Gender	Basketball	Soccer	Total
Boys	52	34	**86**
Girls	29	45	**74**
Total	**81**	**79**	**160**

Use the table to find the cell that represents boys **and** basketball. This is the numerator. The denominator is the grand total.

The joint relative frequency of boys whose favorite sport is basketball is $\frac{52}{160} = 0.325 \approx 0.33$.

Exercises

A survey asked 59 men and 62 women about a ballot proposition in an upcoming election. In the survey, there were 18 men who intend to vote No on the proposition and 32 women who intend to vote Yes.

13. Make a two-way frequency table.

14. Make a two-way relative frequency table.

15. What is the joint relative frequency of a man intending to vote Yes on the proposition?

16. What is the joint relative frequency of a woman intending to vote No on the proposition?

17. What is the marginal relative frequency of a person intending to vote Yes on the proposition?

18. What is the conditional relative frequency that a person surveyed is a man, given that the person intended to vote No on the proposition?

19. What is the conditional relative frequency that a person surveyed is a man, given that the person intended to vote Yes on the proposition?

20. What conclusion can you draw based on the conditional relative frequencies you found?

Pull It All Together

Choosing a Location for a Tournament

Luis is the director of a youth baseball league. He needs to find a location for the league's championship tournament in June. The ideal location should be warm, with as little rain as possible. Luis has narrowed down the choices to two cities: Oakville and Fairview.

For each city, Luis collects data on the average June temperature and the June rainfall. The data are shown in the tables.

Oakville Climate										
Year	2004	2005	2006	2007	2008	2009	2010	2011	2012	2013
Avg. June Temp. (°F)	68	79	72	71	72	75	75	78	77	75
June Rainfall (in.)	2.8	5.1	3.4	3.1	3.6	4.1	3.4	4.9	4.5	4.0

Fairview Climate										
Year	2004	2005	2006	2007	2008	2009	2010	2011	2012	2013
Avg. June Temp. (°F)	67	75	60	73	68	72	61	69	71	71
June Rainfall (in.)	2.5	1.3	3.0	1.5	1.9	1.8	3.3	2.0	2.4	2.0

Task Description

Decide whether the tournament should be held in Oakville or Fairview, and justify your decision.

- How can measures of center, measures of dispersion, and/or data displays help you compare the temperatures in the two cities and the rainfall in the two cities?

- What can you learn from making a scatter plot of each city's data?

Get Ready!

Squaring Numbers

Simplify.

1. 3^2 **2.** 4^2 **3.** 11^2

Simplifying Expressions

Simplify each expression. Use 3.14 for π.

4. $2 \cdot 7.5 + 2 \cdot 11$ **5.** $\pi(5)^2$ **6.** $\sqrt{5^2 + 12^2}$

Evaluating Expressions

Evaluate the following expressions for $a = 4$ and $b = -2$.

7. $\dfrac{a + b}{2}$ **8.** $\dfrac{a - 7}{3 - b}$ **9.** $\sqrt{(7 - a)^2 + (2 - b)^2}$

Finding Absolute Value

Simplify each absolute value expression.

10. $|-8|$ **11.** $|2 - 6|$ **12.** $|-5 - (-8)|$

Solving Equations

Algebra Solve each equation.

13. $2x + 7 = 13$ **14.** $5x - 12 = 2x + 6$ **15.** $2(x + 3) - 1 = 7x$

 # Looking Ahead Vocabulary

16. Artists often use long streaks to show *rays* of light coming from the sun. A *ray* is also a geometric figure. What do you think the properties of a *ray* are?

17. You and your friend work with each other. In other words, you and your friend are *co*-workers. What might the term *collinear* mean in geometry?

Tools of Geometry

Big Ideas

1 Visualization

Essential Question How can you represent a three-dimensional figure with a two-dimensional drawing?

2 Reasoning

Essential Question What are the building blocks of geometry?

3 Measurement

Essential Question How can you describe the attributes of a segment or angle?

© Domains

* Congruence

Chapter Preview

7-1 **Nets and Drawings for Visualizing Geometry**

7-2 **Points, Lines, and Planes**

7-3 **Measuring Segments**

7-4 **Measuring Angles**

7-5 **Exploring Angle Pairs**

7-6 **Midpoint and Distance in the Coordinate Plane**

Interactive Digital Path

Log in to **pearsonsuccessnet.com** and click on Interactive Digital Path to access the Solve Its and animated Problems.

🔊 Vocabulary

English/Spanish Vocabulary Audio Online:

English	Spanish
angle bisector, *p. 471*	bisectriz de un ángulo
congruent segments, *p. 453*	segmentos congruentes
isometric drawing, *p. 433*	dibujo isométrico
linear pair, *p. 469*	par lineal
net, *p. 431*	plantilla
orthographic drawing, *p. 435*	dibujo ortográfico
postulate, *p. 444*	postulado
segment bisector, *p. 454*	bisectriz de un segmento
supplementary angles, *p. 467*	ángulos suplementarios
vertical angles, *p. 466*	ángulos verticales

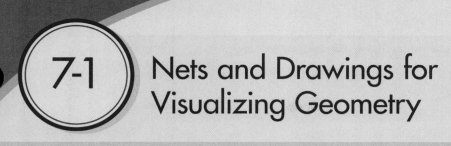

7-1 Nets and Drawings for Visualizing Geometry

Prepares for **MCC9-12.G.CO.1** Know precise definitions of angle, circle, perpendicular line, parallel line, and line segment . . .

Objective To make nets and drawings of three-dimensional figures

Solve It! Write your solution to the Solve It in the space below.

In the Solve It, you had to "see" the projection of one side of an object onto a flat surface. Visualizing figures is a key skill that you will develop in geometry.

Essential Understanding You can represent a three-dimensional object with a two-dimensional figure using special drawing techniques.

A **net** is a two-dimensional diagram that you can fold to form a three-dimensional figure. A net shows all of the surfaces of a figure in one view.

Problem 1 Identifying a Solid From a Net

Got It? The net in Problem 1 folds into the cube shown at the right. Which letters will be on the top and right side of the cube?

Practice Match each three-dimensional figure with its net.

1.

2.

3.

A.

B.

C.

Packaging designers use nets to design boxes and other containers like the box in Problem 2.

 Problem 2 Drawing a Net From a Solid

Think

How can you see the net?

Got It? **a.** What is a net for the figure below? Label the net with its dimensions.

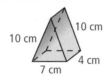

10 cm

10 cm

4 cm

7 cm

b. Reasoning Is there another possible net for the figure in part (a)? If so, draw it.

A Practice Draw a net for each figure. Label the net with its dimensions.

4.

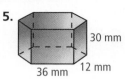

2 in.   2 in.   4 in.

5.

30 mm   36 mm   12 mm

An **isometric drawing** shows a corner view of a three-dimensional figure. It allows you to see the top, front, and side of the figure. You can draw an isometric drawing on isometric dot paper. The simple drawing of a file cabinet at the right is an isometric drawing.

A net shows a three-dimensional figure as a folded-out flat surface. An isometric drawing shows a three-dimensional figure using slanted lines to represent depth.

ONLINE PROBLEMS **Problem 3** Isometric Drawing

Got It? What is an isometric drawing of this cube structure?

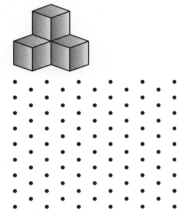

Practice Make an isometric drawing of each cube structure on isometric dot paper.

6.

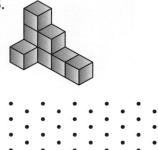

. . . .
. . . .
. . . .
. . . .
. . . .
. . . .
. . . .
. . . .
. . . .

7.

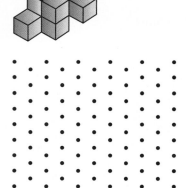

. . . .
. . . .
. . . .
. . . .
. . . .
. . . .
. . . .
. . . .
. . . .
. . . .

An **orthographic drawing** is another way to represent a three-dimensional figure. An orthographic drawing shows three separate views: a top view, a front view, and a right-side view.

Although an orthographic drawing may take more time to analyze, it provides unique information about the shape of a structure.

Problem 4 **Orthographic Drawing**

Got It? What is the orthographic drawing for this isometric drawing?

Plan

How can you determine the top, front, and right-side views?

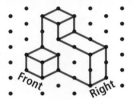

Practice For each isometric drawing in Exercises 8 and 9, make an orthographic drawing. Assume there are no hidden cubes.

8.

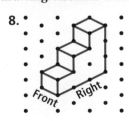

9.

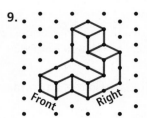

Lesson Check

Do you know HOW?

10. What is a net for the figure below? Label the net with its dimensions.

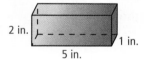

11. What is an isometric drawing of the cube structure?

12. What is the orthographic drawing of the isometric drawing at the right? Assume there are no hidden cubes.

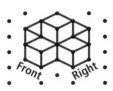

Do you UNDERSTAND?

13. Vocabulary Tell whether each drawing is *isometric*, *orthographic*, a *net*, or *none*.

a.

b.
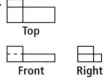

c.
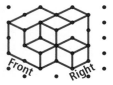

d.

14. Compare and Contrast What are the differences and similarities between an isometric drawing and an orthographic drawing? Explain.

More Practice and Problem-Solving Exercises

B Apply

15. Multiple Representations There are eight different nets for the solid shown at the right. Draw as many of them as you can. (*Hint*: Two nets are the same if you can rotate or flip one to match the other.)

16. a. Open-Ended Make an isometric drawing of a structure that you can build using 8 cubes.
  b. Make an orthographic drawing of this structure.

© 17. **Think About a Plan** Draw a net of the can at the right.
- What shape are the top and bottom of the can?
- If you uncurl the body of the can, what shape do you get?

18. **History** In 1525, German printmaker Albrecht Dürer first used the word *net* to describe a printed pattern that folds up into a three-dimensional shape. Why do you think he chose to use the word *net*?

STEM **Manufacturing** Match the package with its net.

19.

20.

21.

A.

B.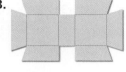

C.

© 22. **Error Analysis** Miquela and Gina drew orthographic drawings for the cube structure at the right. Who is correct?

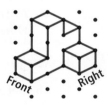

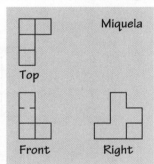

Miquela

Gina

Make an orthographic drawing for each isometric drawing.

23.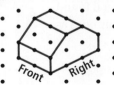

24.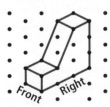

25.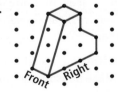

26. Fort Use the diagram of the fort at the right.
  a. Make an isometric drawing of the fort.
  b. Make an orthographic drawing of the fort.

STEM **27. Aerial Photography** Another perspective in aerial photography is the "bird's-eye view," which shows an object from directly overhead. What type of drawing that you have studied in this lesson is a bird's-eye view?

28. Writing Photographs of buildings are typically not taken from a bird's-eye view. Describe a situation in which you would want a photo showing a bird's-eye view.

Visualization Think about how each net can be folded to form a cube. What is the number of the face that will be opposite Face 1?

29.  **30.** 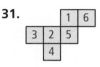 **31.**   **32.**

33. Multiple Representations There are 11 different nets for a cube. Four of them are shown above.
  a. Draw the other seven nets.
  b. **Writing** Suppose you want to make 100 cubes for an art project. Which of the 11 nets would you use? Explain why.

C Challenge

34. The net at the right folds into a cube. Sketch the cube so that its front face is shaded as shown below.

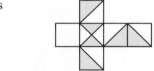

35. Architecture What does a net of the staircase shown look like? Draw the net. (*Hint*: Visualize stretching the stairs out flat.)

36. A hexomino is a two-dimensional figure formed with six squares. Each square shares at least one side with another square. The 11 nets of a cube that you found in Exercise 33 are hexominoes. Draw as many of the remaining 24 hexominoes as you can.

37. Visualization Use the orthographic drawing at the right.
  a. Make an isometric drawing of the structure.
  b. Make an isometric drawing of the structure from part (a) after it has been turned on its base 90° counterclockwise.
  c. Make an orthographic drawing of the structure from part (b).
  d. Turn the structure from part (a) 180°. Repeat parts (b) and (c).

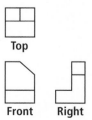

7-2 Points, Lines, and Planes

MCC9-12.G.CO.1 Know precise definitions of . . . and line segment . . . based on the undefined notions of point, line, . . .

Objective To understand basic terms and postulates of geometry

 Solve It! Write your solution to the Solve It in the space below.

In this lesson, you will learn basic geometric facts to help you justify your answer to the Solve It.

Essential Understanding Geometry is a mathematical system built on accepted facts, basic terms, and definitions.

In geometry, some words such as *point, line*, and *plane* are undefined. Undefined terms are the basic ideas that you can use to build the definitions of all other figures in geometry. Although you cannot define undefined terms, it is important to have a general description of their meanings.

take note

Key Concept Undefined Terms

Term Description	How to Name It	Diagram
A **point** indicates a location and has no size.	You can represent a point by a dot and name it by a capital letter, such as *A*.	*A* •
A **line** is represented by a straight path that extends in two opposite directions without end and has no thickness. A line contains infinitely many points.	You can name a line by any two points on the line, such as $\overleftrightarrow{AB}$ (read "line *AB*") or $\overleftrightarrow{BA}$, or by a single lowercase letter, such as line ℓ.	ℓ, B, A
A **plane** is represented by a flat surface that extends without end and has no thickness. A plane contains infinitely many lines.	You can name a plane by a capital letter, such as plane *P*, or by at least three points in the plane that do not all lie on the same line, such as plane *ABC*.	P, A, B, C

Points that lie on the same line are **collinear points**. Points and lines that lie in the same plane are **coplanar**. All the points of a line are coplanar.

Problem 1 **Naming Points, Lines, and Planes**

Got It? **a.** What are two other ways to name $\overleftrightarrow{RS}$?

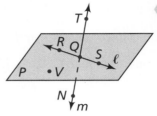

Think

Why can figures have more than one name?

b. What are two more ways to name plane *P*?

c. What are the names of three other collinear points?

d. What are two points that are *not* coplanar with points *R, S,* and *V*?

A Practice Use the figure at the right for Exercises 1 and 2.

1. Name three collinear points.

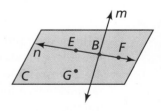

2. Name four coplanar points.

The terms *point, line*, and *plane* are not defined because their definitions would require terms that also need defining. You can, however, use undefined terms to define other terms. A geometric figure is a set of points. **Space** is the set of all points in three dimensions. Similarly, the definitions for *segment* and *ray* are based on points and lines.

Key Concept   Defined Terms

Definition	How to Name It	Diagram
A **segment** is part of a line that consists of two endpoints and all points between them.	You can name a segment by its two endpoints, such as $\overline{AB}$ (read "segment AB") or $\overline{BA}$.	A ———— B
A **ray** is part of a line that consists of one endpoint and all the points of the line on one side of the endpoint.	You can name a ray by its endpoint and another point on the ray, such as $\overrightarrow{AB}$ (read "ray AB"). The order of points indicates the ray's direction.	A ———→ B
Opposite rays are two rays that share the same endpoint and form a line.	You can name opposite rays by their shared endpoint and any other point on each ray, such as $\overrightarrow{CA}$ and $\overrightarrow{CB}$.	←— A C B —→

 Problem 2   Naming Segments and Rays

Got It?   **Reasoning** $\overrightarrow{EF}$ and $\overrightarrow{FE}$ form a line. Are they opposite rays? Explain.

Think

How do you know if two rays are opposite rays?

Ⓐ Practice   Use the figure at the right for Exercises 3 and 4.

3. What are all the segments you can name in the figure?

4. What are all the rays you can name in the figure?

A **postulate** or **axiom** is an accepted statement of fact. Postulates, like undefined terms, are basic building blocks of the logical system in geometry. You will use logical reasoning to prove general concepts in this book.

You have used some of the following geometry postulates in algebra. For example, you used Postulate 1 when you graphed equations such as $y = 2x + 8$. You graphed two points and drew the line through the points.

take note

Postulate 1

Through any two points there is exactly one line.

Line t passes through points A and B. Line t is the only line that passes through both points.

When you have two or more geometric figures, their **intersection** is the set of points the figures have in common.

In algebra, one way to solve a system of two equations is to graph them. The graphs of the two lines $y = -2x + 8$ and $y = 3x - 7$ intersect in a single point, (3, 2). So the solution is (3, 2). This illustrates Postulate 2.

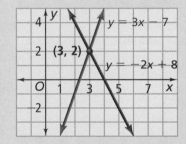

take note

Postulate 2

If two distinct lines intersect, then they intersect in exactly one point.

$\overleftrightarrow{AE}$ and $\overleftrightarrow{DB}$ intersect in point C.

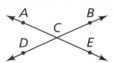

There is a similar postulate about the intersection of planes.

take note

Postulate 3

If two distinct planes intersect, then they intersect in exactly one line.

Plane RST and plane WST intersect in $\overleftrightarrow{ST}$.

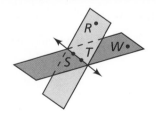

When you know two points that two planes have in common, Postulates 1 and 3 tell you that the line through those points is the intersection of the planes.

Problem 3 **Finding the Intersection of Two Planes**

Got It? **a.** What are the names of two planes that intersect in $\overleftrightarrow{BF}$?

b. Reasoning Why do you only need to find two common points to name the intersection of two distinct planes?

Practice Use the figure at the right for Exercises 5 and 6.

5. Name the intersection of planes *QRS* and *RSW*.

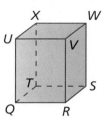

6. Name two planes that intersect in $\overleftrightarrow{QU}$.

When you name a plane from a figure like the box in Problem 3, list the corner points in consecutive order. For example, plane *ADCB* and plane *ABCD* are also names for the plane on the top of the box. Plane *ACBD* is not.

Photographers use three-legged tripods to make sure that a camera is steady. The feet of the tripod all touch the floor at the same time. You can think of the feet as points and the floor as a plane. As long as the feet do not all lie in one line, they will lie in exactly one plane.

This illustrates Postulate 4.

 take note

Postulate 4

Through any three noncollinear points there is exactly one plane.

Points Q, R, and S are noncollinear. Plane P is the only plane that contains them.

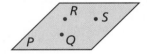

Problem 4 | **Using Postulate 4**

Got It? **a.** What plane contains points L, M, and N? Shade the plane in the figure below.

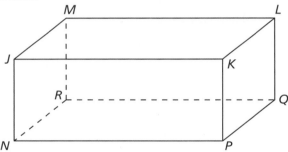

ⓒ **b. Reasoning** What is the name of a line that is coplanar with $\overleftrightarrow{JK}$ and $\overleftrightarrow{KL}$?

Practice Shade the plane that contains the given points.

7. *R, V, W*

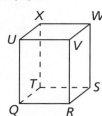

8. *U, V, W*

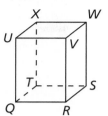

 Lesson Check

Do you know HOW?

Use the figure at the right.

9. What are two other names for $\overleftrightarrow{XY}$?

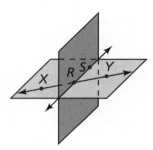

10. What are the opposite rays?

11. What is the intersection of the two planes?

Do you UNDERSTAND?

12. Vocabulary A segment has endpoints R and S. What are two names for the segment?

13. Are $\overrightarrow{AB}$ and $\overrightarrow{BA}$ the same ray? Explain.

14. Reasoning Why do you use two arrowheads when drawing or naming a line such as $\overleftrightarrow{EF}$?

15. Compare and Contrast How is naming a ray similar to naming a line? How is it different?

More Practice and Problem-Solving Exercises

B Apply

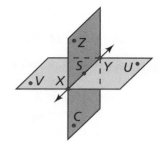

Postulate 4 states that any three noncollinear points lie in exactly one plane. Find the plane that contains the first three points listed. Then determine whether the fourth point is in that plane. Write coplanar or noncoplanar to describe the points.

16. Z, S, Y, C

17. S, U, V, Y

18. X, Y, Z, U

19. X, S, V, U

20. X, Z, S, V

21. S, V, C, Y

If possible, draw a figure to fit each description. Otherwise, write *not possible*.

22. four points that are collinear

23. two points that are noncollinear

24. three points that are noncollinear

25. three points that are noncoplanar

ⓒ 26. Open-Ended Draw a figure with points B, C, D, E, F, and G that shows $\overleftrightarrow{CD}$, $\overleftrightarrow{BG}$, and $\overleftrightarrow{EF}$, with one of the points on all three lines.

ⓒ 27. Think About a Plan Your friend drew the diagram at the right to prove to you that two planes can intersect in exactly one point. Describe your friend's error.
- How do you describe a plane?
- What does it mean for two planes to intersect each other?
- Can you define an endpoint of a plane?

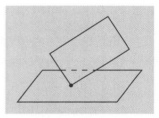

ⓒ 28. Reasoning If one ray contains another ray, are they the same ray? Explain.

For Exercises 29–34, determine whether each statement is *always*, *sometimes*, or *never* true.

29. $\overleftrightarrow{TQ}$ and $\overleftrightarrow{QT}$ are the same line.

30. $\overrightarrow{JK}$ and $\overrightarrow{JL}$ are the same ray.

31. Intersecting lines are coplanar.

32. Four points are coplanar.

33. A plane containing two points of a line contains the entire line.

34. Two distinct lines intersect in more than one point.

ⓒ 35. Use the diagram at the right. How many planes contain each line and point?
- **a.** $\overleftrightarrow{EF}$ and point G
- **b.** $\overleftrightarrow{PH}$ and point E
- **c.** $\overleftrightarrow{FG}$ and point P
- **d.** $\overleftrightarrow{EP}$ and point G
- **e. Reasoning** What do you think is true of a line and a point not on the line? Explain. (*Hint*: Use two of the postulates you learned in this lesson.)

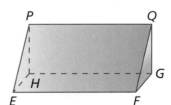

In Exercises 36–38, sketch a figure for the given information. Then state the postulate that your figure illustrates.

36. $\overleftrightarrow{AB}$ and $\overleftrightarrow{EF}$ intersect in point C.

37. The noncollinear points A, B, and C are all contained in plane N.

38. Planes LNP and MVK intersect in $\overleftrightarrow{NM}$.

STEM **39. Telecommunications** A cell phone tower at point A receives a cell phone signal from the southeast. A cell phone tower at point B receives a signal from the same cell phone from due west. Trace the diagram at the right and find the location of the cell phone. Describe how Postulates 1 and 2 help you locate the phone.

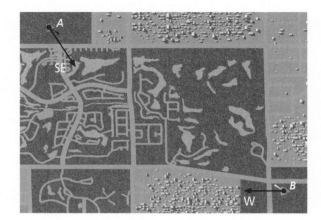

40. Estimation You can represent the hands on a clock at 6:00 as opposite rays. Estimate the other 11 times on a clock that you can represent as opposite rays.

41. Open-Ended What are some basic words in English that are difficult to define?

Coordinate Geometry Graph the points and state whether they are collinear.

42. $(1, 1), (4, 4), (-3, -3)$ **43.** $(2, 4), (4, 6), (0, 2)$

44. $(0, 0), (-5, 1), (6, -2)$ **45.** $(0, 0), (8, 10), (4, 6)$

46. $(0, 0), (0, 3), (0, -10)$ **47.** $(-2, -6), (1, -2), (4, 1)$

Challenge

48. How many planes contain the same three collinear points? Explain.

49. How many planes contain a given line? Explain.

50. a. Writing Suppose two points are in plane P. Explain why the line containing the points is also in plane P.
  b. Reasoning Suppose two lines intersect. How many planes do you think contain both lines? Use the diagram at the right and your answer to part (a) to explain your answer.

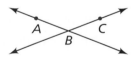

7-3 Measuring Segments

MCC9-12.G.CO.1 Know precise definitions . . . based on the undefined notions of point, line, distance along a line, and distance around a circular arc. Also **MCC9-12.G.GPE.6**

Objective To find and compare lengths of segments

Solve It! Write your solution to the Solve It in the space below.

In the Solve It, you measured the length of an object indirectly.

Essential Understanding You can use number operations to find and compare the lengths of segments.

take note

Postulate 5   Ruler Postulate

Every point on a line can be paired with a real number. This makes a one-to-one correspondence between the points on the line and the real numbers. The real number that corresponds to a point is called the **coordinate** of the point.

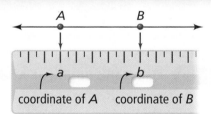

The Ruler Postulate allows you to measure lengths of segments using a given unit and to find distances between points on a number line. Consider $\overleftrightarrow{AB}$ at the right. The **distance** between points A and B is the absolute value of the difference of their coordinates, or $|a - b|$. This value is also AB, or the length of $\overline{AB}$.

$$AB = |a - b|$$

Problem 1 **Measuring Segment Lengths**

Got It? What are *UV* and *SV* on the number line below?

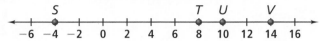

 Practice Find the length of each segment.

1. $\overline{BD}$　　　　　　　　　**2.** $\overline{CE}$

---

take note

Postulate 6 **Segment Addition Postulate**

If three points *A*, *B*, and *C* are collinear and *B* is between *A* and *C*, then $AB + BC = AC$.

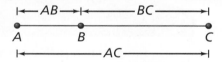

 Problem 2 **Using the Segment Addition Postulate**

Plan

How can you use algebra to solve this problem?

Got It? In the diagram, $JL = 120$. What are *JK* and *KL*?

$$\underset{J \qquad\quad K \qquad\qquad L}{\overset{4x+6 \qquad\quad 7x+15}{\rule{5cm}{0.4pt}}}$$

Practice Use the number line at the right for Exercises 3 and 4.

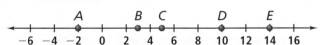

3. If $RS = 15$ and $ST = 9$, then what is RT?

4. If $ST = 15$ and $RT = 40$, then what is RS?

When numerical expressions have the same value, you say that they are equal (=). Similarly, if two segments have the same length, then the segments are **congruent** (≅) **segments**.

This means that if $AB = CD$, then $\overline{AB} \cong \overline{CD}$. You can also say that if $\overline{AB} \cong \overline{CD}$, then $AB = CD$.

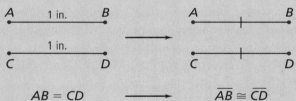

$$AB = CD \longrightarrow \overline{AB} \cong \overline{CD}$$

As illustrated above, you can mark segments alike to show that they are congruent. If there is more than one set of congruent segments, you can indicate each set with the same number of marks.

ONLINE PROBLEMS

Problem 3   **Comparing Segment Lengths**

Plan

Got It?   **a.** Is $\overline{AB}$ congruent to $\overline{DE}$?

How do you know if two segments are congruent?

b. Reasoning To find AC, suppose you subtract -2 from 5. Do you get the same result as subtracting 5 from -2? Why?

Ⓐ Practice Use the number line below for Exercises 5 and 6. Tell whether the segments are congruent.

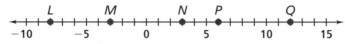

5. $\overline{LN}$ and $\overline{MQ}$ **6.** $\overline{MP}$ and $\overline{NQ}$

The **midpoint** of a segment is a point that divides the segment into two congruent segments. A point, line, ray, or other segment that intersects a segment at its midpoint is said to *bisect* the segment. That point, line, ray, or segment is called a **segment bisector**.

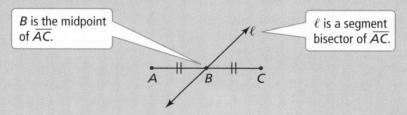

B is the midpoint of $\overline{AC}$.

ℓ is a segment bisector of $\overline{AC}$.

Problem 4 **Using the Midpoint**

Got It? **a. Reasoning** In Problem 4, is it necessary to substitute 8 for x in the expression for QR in order to find QR? Explain.

b. U is the midpoint of $\overline{TV}$. What are TU, UV, and TV?

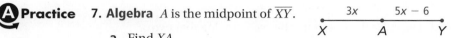

 Practice   **7. Algebra** A is the midpoint of $\overline{XY}$.

a. Find XA.

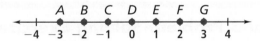

b. Find AY and XY.

Lesson Check

Do you know HOW?

Name each of the following.

8. The point on $\overrightarrow{DA}$ that is 2 units from D

9. Two points that are 3 units from D

10. The coordinate of the midpoint of $\overline{AG}$

11. A segment congruent to $\overline{AC}$

Do you UNDERSTAND?

@ **12. Vocabulary** Name two segment bisectors of $\overline{PR}$.

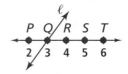

@ **13. Compare and Contrast** Describe the difference between saying that two segments are *congruent* and saying that two segments have *equal length*. When would you use each phrase?

@ **14. Error Analysis** You and your friend live 5 mi apart. He says that it is 5 mi from his house to your house and −5 mi from your house to his house. What is the error in his argument?

More Practice and Problem-Solving Exercises

 Apply

On a number line, the coordinates of X, Y, Z, and W are -7, -3, 1, and 5, respectively. Find the lengths of the two segments. Then tell whether they are congruent.

15. $\overline{XY}$ and $\overline{ZW}$ **16.** $\overline{ZX}$ and $\overline{WY}$ **17.** $\overline{YZ}$ and $\overline{XW}$

Suppose the coordinate of A is 0, $AR = 5$, and $AT = 7$. What are the possible coordinates of the midpoint of the given segment?

18. $\overline{AR}$ **19.** $\overline{AT}$ **20.** $\overline{RT}$

21. Suppose point E has a coordinate of 3 and $EG = 5$. What are the possible coordinates of point G?

Visualization Without using your ruler, sketch a segment with the given length. Use your ruler to see how well your sketch approximates the length provided.

22. 3 cm   **23.** 3 in.   **24.** 6 in.   **25.** 10 cm   **26.** 65 mm

27. Think About a Plan The numbers labeled on the map of Florida are mile markers. Assume that Route 10 between Quincy and Jacksonville is straight.

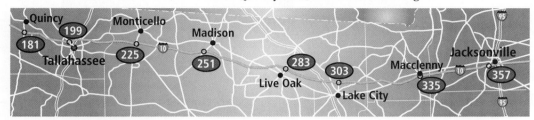

Suppose you drive at an average speed of 55 mi/h. How long will it take to get from Live Oak to Jacksonville?
  • How can you use mile markers to find distances between points?
  • How do average speed, distance, and time all relate to each other?

28. On a number line, A is at -2 and B is at 4. What is the coordinate of C, which is $\frac{2}{3}$ of the way from A to B?

Error Analysis Use the highway sign for Exercises 29 and 30.

29. A driver reads the highway sign and says, "It's 145 miles from Mitchell to Watertown." What error did the driver make? Explain.

30. Your friend reads the highway sign and says, "It's 71 miles to Watertown." Is your friend correct? Explain.

Algebra Use the diagram at the right for Exercises 31 and 32.

31. If $AD = 12$ and $AC = 4y - 36$, find the value of y. Then find AC and DC.

32. If $ED = x + 4$ and $DB = 3x - 8$, find ED, DB, and EB.

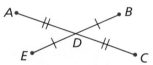

33. Writing Suppose you know PQ and QR. Can you use the Segment Addition Postulate to find PR? Explain.

Challenge

34. C is the midpoint of $\overline{AB}$, D is the midpoint of $\overline{AC}$, E is the midpoint of $\overline{AD}$, F is the midpoint of $\overline{ED}$, G is the midpoint of $\overline{EF}$, and H is the midpoint of $\overline{DB}$. If $DC = 16$, what is GH?

35. a. Algebra Use the diagram at the right. What algebraic expression represents GK?
   b. If $GK = 30$, what are GH and JK?

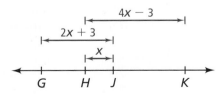

7-4 | Measuring Angles

MCC9-12.G.CO.1 Know precise definitions of angle, circle, perpendicular line, parallel line . . . based on the undefined notions of point, line, distance along a line . . .

Objective   To find and compare the measures of angles

 Solve It!   Write your solution to the Solve It in the space below.

In this lesson, you will learn to describe and measure angles like the ones in the Solve It.

Essential Understanding   You can use number operations to find and compare the measures of angles.

Key Concept   Angle

Definition	**How to Name It**	**Diagram**
An **angle** is formed by two rays with the same endpoint. The **rays** are the sides of the angle. The endpoint is the **vertex** of the angle.	You can name an angle by • its vertex, $\angle A$ • a point on each ray and the vertex, $\angle BAC$ or $\angle CAB$ • a number, $\angle 1$	 The sides of the angle are $\overrightarrow{AB}$ and $\overrightarrow{AC}$. The vertex is A.

When you name angles using three points, the vertex must go in the middle.

The *interior* of an angle is the region containing all of the points between the two sides of the angle. The *exterior* of an angle is the region containing all of the points outside of the angle.

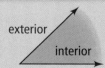

Got It? **a.** What are two other names for ∠KML?

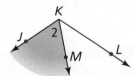 **b. Reasoning** Would it be correct to name any of the angles ∠M? Explain.

 Practice Name each shaded angle in three different ways.

1.

2.

One way to measure the size of an angle is in degrees. To indicate the measure of an angle, write a lowercase *m* in front of the angle symbol. In the diagram, the measure of ∠A is 62. You write this as $m\angle A = 62$. In this book, you will work only with degree measures.

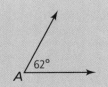

A **circle** is the set of all points in a plane that are a given distance from a given point. A circle has 360°, so 1 degree is $\frac{1}{360}$ of a circle. A protractor forms half a circle and measures angles from 0° to 180°.

Postulate 7   Protractor Postulate

Consider $\overrightarrow{OB}$ and a point A on one side of $\overleftrightarrow{OB}$. Every ray of the form $\overrightarrow{OA}$ can be paired one-to-one with a real number from 0 to 180.

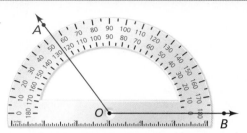

The Protractor Postulate allows you to find the measure of an angle. Consider the diagram below. The **measure** of $\angle COD$ is the absolute value of the difference of the real numbers paired with $\overrightarrow{OC}$ and $\overrightarrow{OD}$. That is, if $\overrightarrow{OC}$ corresponds with c, and $\overrightarrow{OD}$ corresponds with d, then $m\angle COD = |c - d|$.

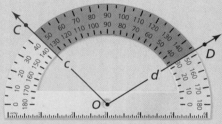

Notice that the Protractor Postulate and the calculation of an angle measure are very similar to the Ruler Postulate and the calculation of a segment length.

You can classify angles according to their measures.

Key Concept   Types of Angles

acute angle	right angle	obtuse angle	straight angle
$0 < x < 90$	$x = 90$	$90 < x < 180$	$x = 180$

The symbol ⌐ in the diagram above indicates a right angle.

Problem 2 **Measuring and Classifying Angles**

Got It? Use the figure in Problem 2. What are the measures of ∠*LKH*, ∠*HKN*, and ∠*MKH*? Classify each angle as *acute*, *right*, *obtuse*, or *straight*.

Think

How do you know whether to use the outer or inner scale on the protractor?

Ⓐ Practice Use the diagram below. Find the measure of each angle. Then classify the angle as *acute*, *right*, *obtuse*, or *straight*.

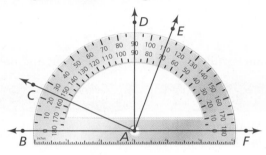

3. ∠*DAF*   **4.** ∠*BAC*   **5.** ∠*DAE*

Angles with the same measure are **congruent angles**. This means that if $m\angle A = m\angle B$, then $\angle A \cong \angle B$. You can also say that if $\angle A \cong \angle B$, then $m\angle A = m\angle B$.

You can mark angles with arcs to show that they are congruent. If there is more than one set of congruent angles, each set is marked with the same number of arcs.

$$m\angle A = m\angle B$$
$$\angle A \cong \angle B$$

Problem 3 **Using Congruent Angles**

Got It? Use the figure in Problem 3. If $m\angle ABC = 49$, what is $m\angle DEF$?

Ⓐ Practice Use the diagram at the right. Complete each statement.

6. If $m\angle EFD = 75$, then $m\angle JAB =$ _____ .

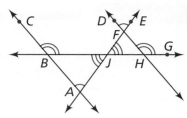

7. If $m\angle GHF = 130$, then $m\angle JBC =$ _____ .

The Angle Addition Postulate is similar to the Segment Addition Postulate.

take note

Postulate 8   Angle Addition Postulate

If point B is in the interior of $\angle AOC$,
then $m\angle AOB + m\angle BOC = m\angle AOC$.

Problem 4   **Using the Angle Addition Postulate**

Plan

How can you use the expressions in the diagram?

Got It? $\angle DEF$ is a straight angle. What are $m\angle DEC$ and $m\angle CEF$?

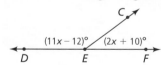

Ⓐ Practice   **8.** If $m\angle ABD = 79$, what are $m\angle ABC$ and $m\angle DBC$?

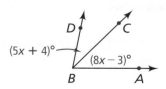

9. $\angle RQT$ is a straight angle. What are $m\angle RQS$ and $m\angle TQS$?

$(6x + 20)°$ $(2x + 4)°$

T Q R

Lesson Check

Do you know HOW?

Use the diagram for Exercises 10–12.

10. What are two other names for $\angle 1$?

11. Algebra If $m\angle ABD = 85$, what is an expression to represent $m\angle ABC$?

12. Classify $\angle ABC$.

Do you UNDERSTAND?

© **13. Vocabulary** How many sides can two congruent angles share? Explain.

© **14. Error Analysis** Your classmate concludes from the diagram at the right that $\angle JKL \cong \angle LKM$. Is your classmate correct? Explain.

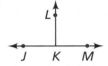

More Practice and Problem-Solving Exercises

B Apply

Use a protractor. Measure and classify each angle.

15.

16.

17.

18.

© **19. Think About a Plan** A pair of earrings has dark-colored wedges that are all the same size. One earring has a 25° light-colored wedge. The other has a 14° light-colored wedge. Find the angle measure of a dark-colored wedge.
  • How do the angle measures of the earrings relate?
  • How can you use algebra to solve the problem?

Algebra Use the diagram at the right for Exercises 20 and 21. Solve for *x*. Find the angle measures to check your work.

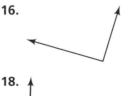

20. $m\angle AOB = 4x - 2$, $m\angle BOC = 5x + 10$, $m\angle COD = 2x + 14$

21. $m\angle AOB = 28$, $m\angle BOC = 3x - 2$, $m\angle AOD = 6x$

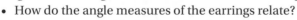

22. If $m\angle MQV = 90$, which expression can you use to find $m\angle VQP$?

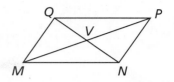

A $m\angle MQP - 90$

C $m\angle MQP + 90$

B $90 - m\angle MQV$

D $90 + m\angle VQP$

23. Literature According to legend, King Arthur and his knights sat around the Round Table to discuss matters of the kingdom. The photo shows a round table on display at Winchester Castle, in England. From the center of the table, each section has the same degree measure. If King Arthur occupied two of these sections, what is the total degree measure of his section?

Ⓒ Challenge

Time Find the angle measure of the hands of a clock at each time.

24. 6:00

25. 7:00

26. 11:00

27. 4:40

28. 5:20

29. 2:15

© **30. Open-Ended** Sketch a right angle with vertex V. Name it $\angle 1$. Then sketch a $135°$ angle that shares a side with $\angle 1$. Name it $\angle PVB$. Is there more than one way to sketch $\angle PVB$? If so, sketch all the different possibilities. (*Hint:* Two angles are the same if you can rotate or flip one to match the other.)

© **31. Technology** Your classmate constructs an angle. Then he constructs a ray from the vertex of the angle to a point in the interior of the angle. He measures all the angles formed. Then he moves the interior ray as shown below. What postulate do the two pictures support?

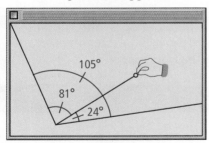
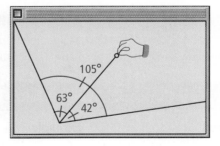

7-5 Exploring Angle Pairs

MCC9-12.G.CO.1 Know precise definitions of angle . . .

Objective To identify special angle pairs and use their relationships to find angle measures

 Solve It! Write your solution to the Solve It in the space below.

In this lesson, you will learn how to describe different kinds of angle pairs.

Essential Understanding Special angle pairs can help you identify geometric relationships. You can use these angle pairs to find angle measures.

take note ➤ Key Concept Types of Angle Pairs

Definition	Example
Adjacent angles are two coplanar angles with a common side, a common vertex, and no common interior points.	∠1 and ∠2, ∠3 and ∠4
Vertical angles are two angles whose sides are opposite rays.	∠1 and ∠2, ∠3 and ∠4

Key Concept   Types of Angle Pairs

Definition	Example	

Complementary angles are two angles whose measures have a sum of 90. Each angle is called the *complement* of the other.

∠1 and ∠2, ∠A and ∠B

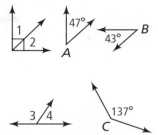

Supplementary angles are two angles whose measures have a sum of 180. Each angle is called the *supplement* of the other.

∠3 and ∠4, ∠B and ∠C

Problem 1   Identifying Angle Pairs

Got It?   Use the diagram at the right. Is the statement true? Explain.

a. ∠AFE and ∠CFD are vertical angles.

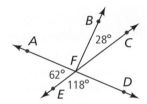

b. ∠BFC and ∠DFE are supplementary.

c. ∠BFD and ∠AFB are adjacent angles.

Think

What conditions must be met for two angles to be adjacent angles?

Practice Name an angle or angles in the diagram described by each of the following. Use the figure at the right.

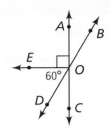

1. complementary to ∠EOD

2. a pair of vertical angles

take note

Concept Summary Finding Information From a Diagram

There are some relationships you can assume to be true from a diagram that has no marks or measures. There are other relationships you cannot assume directly. For example, you *can* conclude the following from an unmarked diagram.

- Angles are adjacent.
- Angles are adjacent and supplementary.
- Angles are vertical angles.

You *cannot* conclude the following from an unmarked diagram.

- Angles or segments are congruent.
- An angle is a right angle.
- Angles are complementary.

Problem 2 Making Conclusions From a Diagram

Got It? Can you make each conclusion from the information in the diagram? Explain.

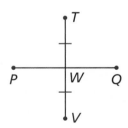

a. $\overline{TW} \cong \overline{WV}$

b. $\overline{PW} \cong \overline{WQ}$

c. ∠*TWQ* is a right angle.

d. $\overline{TV}$ bisects $\overline{PQ}$.

Ⓐ Practice For Exercises 3 and 4, can you make each conclusion from the information in the diagram? Explain.

3. ∠*J* ≅ ∠*D*

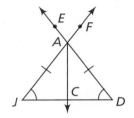

4. *C* is the midpoint of $\overline{JD}$.

A **linear pair** is a pair of adjacent angles whose noncommon sides are opposite rays. The angles of a linear pair form a straight angle.

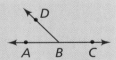

take note

Postulate 9   Linear Pair Postulate

If two angles form a linear pair, then they are supplementary.

Problem 3   **Finding Missing Angle Measures**

Got It?   **a. Reasoning** How can you check your results in Problem 3?

   b. $\angle ADB$ and $\angle BDC$ are a linear pair. $m\angle ADB = 3x + 14$ and
   $m\angle BDC = 5x - 2$. What are $m\angle ADB$ and $m\angle BDC$?

Practice   **5.** Name two pairs of angles that form a linear pair in the
   diagram at the right.

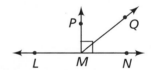

   6. $\angle EFG$ and $\angle GFH$ are a linear pair, $m\angle EFG = 2n + 21$, and
   $m\angle GFH = 4n + 15$. What are $m\angle EFG$ and $m\angle GFH$?

An **angle bisector** is a ray that divides an angle into two congruent angles. Its endpoint is at the angle vertex. Within the ray, a segment with the same endpoint is also an angle bisector. The ray or segment bisects the angle. In the diagram, $\overrightarrow{AY}$ is the angle bisector of $\angle XAZ$, so $\angle XAY \cong \angle YAZ$.

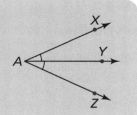

 Problem 4 **Using an Angle Bisector to Find Angle Measures**

Got It? $\overrightarrow{KM}$ bisects $\angle JKL$. If $m\angle JKL = 72$, what is $m\angle JKM$?

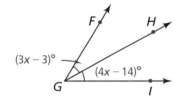

Plan

How can a diagram help you visualize the given information?

Ⓐ **Practice** 7. **Algebra** In the diagram, $\overrightarrow{GH}$ bisects $\angle FGI$.

a. Solve for x and find $m\angle FGH$.

b. Find $m\angle HGI$.

c. Find $m\angle FGI$.

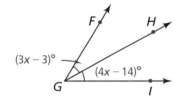

Lesson Check

Do you know HOW?

Name a pair of the following types of angle pairs.

8. vertical angles

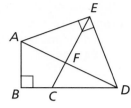

9. complementary angles

10. linear pair

11. $\overrightarrow{PB}$ bisects $\angle RPT$ so that $m\angle RPB = x + 2$ and $m\angle TPB = 2x - 6$. What is $m\angle RPT$?

Do you UNDERSTAND?

12. Vocabulary How does the term *linear pair* describe how the angle pair looks?

13. Error Analysis Your friend calculated the value of x below. What is her error?

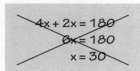

4x + 2x = 180
6x = 180
x = 30

$2x°$

$4x°$

More Practice and Problem-Solving Exercises

MATHEMATICAL
PRACTICES

B Apply

Algebra $\overrightarrow{BD}$ bisects $\angle ABC$. **Solve for x and find $m\angle ABC$.**

14. $m\angle ABD = 5x, m\angle DBC = 3x + 10$

15. $m\angle ABC = 4x - 12, m\angle ABD = 24$

16. $m\angle ABD = 4x - 16, m\angle CBD = 2x + 6$

17. $m\angle ABD = 3x + 20, m\angle CBD = 6x - 16$

Algebra In exercises 18 and 19, find the measure of each angle in the angle pair described.

18. Think About a Plan The measure of one angle is twice the measure of its supplement.
  • How many angles are there? What is their relationship?
  • How can you use algebra, such as using the variable x, to help you?

19. The measure of one angle is 20 less than the measure of its complement.

In the diagram at the right, $m\angle ACB = 65$. Find each of the following.

20. $m\angle ACD$ **21.** $m\angle BCD$

22. $m\angle ECD$ **23.** $m\angle ACE$

24. Algebra $\angle RQS$ and $\angle TQS$ are a linear pair where $m\angle RQS = 2x + 4$ and $m\angle TQS = 6x + 20$.
  a. Solve for x.
  b. Find $m\angle RQS$ and $m\angle TQS$.
  c. Show how you can check your answer.

25. Writing In the diagram at the right, are ∠1 and ∠2 adjacent? Justify your reasoning.

26. Reasoning When $\overrightarrow{BX}$ bisects ∠ABC, ∠ABX ≅ ∠CBX. One student claims there is always a related equation $m\angle ABX = \frac{1}{2}m\angle ABC$. Another student claims the related equation is $2m\angle ABX = m\angle ABC$. Who is correct? Explain.

STEM 27. Optics A beam of light and a mirror can be used to study the behavior of light. Light that strikes the mirror is reflected so that the angle of reflection and the angle of incidence are congruent. In the diagram, ∠ABC has a measure of 41.
  a. Name the angle of reflection and find its measure.
  b. Find $m\angle ABD$.
  c. Find $m\angle ABE$ and $m\angle DBF$.

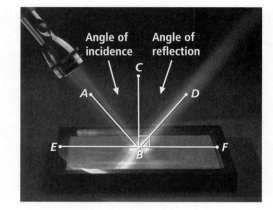

28. Reasoning Describe all situations where vertical angles are also supplementary.

Challenge

Name all of the angle(s) in the diagram described by the following.

29. supplementary to ∠JQM

30. adjacent and congruent to ∠KMQ

31. a linear pair with ∠LMQ

32. complementary to ∠NMR

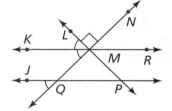

33. Coordinate Geometry The *x*- and *y*-axes of the coordinate plane form four right angles. The interior of each of the right angles is a quadrant of the coordinate plane. What is the equation for the line that contains the angle bisector of Quadrants I and III?

34. $\overrightarrow{XC}$ bisects ∠AXB, $\overrightarrow{XD}$ bisects ∠AXC, $\overrightarrow{XE}$ bisects ∠AXD, $\overrightarrow{XF}$ bisects ∠EXD, $\overrightarrow{XG}$ bisects ∠EXF, and $\overrightarrow{XH}$ bisects ∠DXB. If $m\angle DXC = 16$, find $m\angle GXH$.

7-6

Midpoint and Distance in the Coordinate Plane

Prepares for **MCC9-12.G.GPE.7** Use coordinates to compute perimeters . . . and areas . . . Also prepares for **MCC9-12.G.CO.10**, prepares for **MCC9-12.G.GPE.4**

Objectives To find the midpoint of a segment
To find the distance between two points in the coordinate plane

Solve It! Write your solution to the Solve It in the space below.

In this lesson, you will learn how to find midpoints and distance on a grid like the one in the Solve It.

Essential Understanding You can use formulas to find the midpoint and length of any segment in the coordinate plane.

take note

Key Concept Midpoint Formulas

Description	Formula	Diagram
On a Number Line The coordinate of the midpoint is the *average* or *mean* of the coordinates of the endpoints.	The coordinate of the midpoint M of $\overline{AB}$ is $\frac{a+b}{2}$.	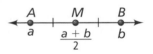
In the Coordinate Plane The coordinates of the midpoint are the average of the x-coordinates and the average of the y-coordinates of the endpoints.	Given $\overline{AB}$ where $A(x_1, y_1)$ and $B(x_2, y_2)$, the coordinates of the midpoint of $\overline{AB}$ are $M\left(\frac{x_1+x_2}{2}, \frac{y_1+y_2}{2}\right)$.	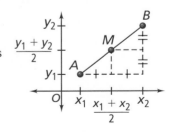

Lesson 7-6 Midpoint and Distance in the Coordinate Plane **475**

Problem 1   **Finding the Midpoint**

Got It?   **a.** $\overline{JK}$ has endpoints at -12 and 4 on a number line. What is the coordinate of its midpoint?

Plan

How do you decide which midpoint formula to use?

b. What is the midpoint of $\overline{RS}$ with endpoints $R(5, -10)$ and $S(3, 6)$?

Ⓐ **Practice**   Find the coordinates of the midpoint of $\overline{HX}$.

1. $H(7, 10), X(5, -8)$

2. $H\left(5\frac{1}{2}, -4\frac{3}{4}\right), X\left(2\frac{1}{4}, -1\frac{1}{4}\right)$

When you know the midpoint and an endpoint of a segment, you can use the Midpoint Formula to find the other endpoint.

Problem 2 **Finding an Endpoint**

Got It? The midpoint of $\overline{AB}$ has coordinates $(4, -9)$. Endpoint A has coordinates $(-3, -5)$. What are the coordinates of B?

Ⓐ Practice The coordinates of point T are given. The midpoint of $\overline{ST}$ is $(5, -8)$. Find the coordinates of point S.

3. $T(1, 12)$

4. $T(4.5, -2.5)$

In Lesson 7-3, you learned how to find the distance between two points on a number line. To find the distance between two points in a coordinate plane, you can use the Distance Formula.

take note

Key Concept **Distance Formula**

The distance between two points $A(x_1, y_1)$ and $B(x_2, y_2)$ is

$$d = \sqrt{(x_2 - x_1)^2 + (y_2 - y_1)^2}$$

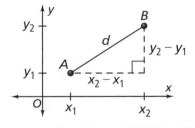

The Distance Formula is based on the *Pythagorean Theorem*. When you use the Distance Formula, you are really finding the length of a side of a right triangle.

$$a^2 + b^2 = c^2$$

Problem 3 **Finding Distance**

Got It?   **a.** $\overline{SR}$ has endpoints $S(-2, 14)$ and $R(3, -1)$. What is SR to the nearest tenth?

⊚ **b. Reasoning** In Problem 3, suppose you let $V(4, -3)$ be (x_1, y_1) and $U(-7, 5)$ be (x_2, y_2). Do you get the same result? Why?

Ⓐ Practice Find the distance between each pair of points. If necessary, round to the nearest tenth.

5. $R(0, 5)$, $S(12, 3)$

6. $X(-3, -4)$, $Y(5, 5)$

Got It?   Use the figure in Problem 4. How far do you travel from
Platform *D* to Platform *E*?

Think

How can a right
triangle involving
points *D* and *E*
help you?

 Practice   Maps For Exercises 7 and 8, use the map at the
right. Find the distance between the cities to
the nearest tenth.

   7. Brookline and Charleston

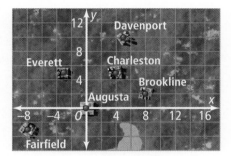

   8. Everett and Fairfield

Lesson Check

Do you know HOW?

  9. $\overline{RS}$ has endpoints $R(2, 4)$ and $S(-1, 7)$. What are the coordinates of its
midpoint M?

10. The midpoint of $\overline{BC}$ is $(5, -2)$. One endpoint is $B(3, 4)$. What are the coordinates of endpoint C?

11. What is the distance between points $K(-9, 8)$ and $L(-6, 0)$?

Do you UNDERSTAND?

12. Reasoning How does the Distance Formula ensure that the distance between two different points is positive?

13. Error Analysis Your friend calculates the distance between points $Q(1, 5)$ and $R(3, 8)$. What is his error?

$$d = \sqrt{(1-8)^2 + (5-3)^2}$$
$$= \sqrt{(-7)^2 + 2^2}$$
$$= \sqrt{49 + 4}$$
$$= \sqrt{53} \approx 7.3$$

More Practice and Problem-Solving Exercises

 MATHEMATICAL PRACTICES

B Apply

Find (a) *PQ* to the nearest tenth and (b) the coordinates of the midpoint of $\overline{PQ}$.

14. $P(3, 2), Q(6, 6)$ **15.** $P(0, -2), Q(3, 3)$ **16.** $P(-4, -2), Q(1, 3)$

17. $P(-5, 2), Q(0, 4)$ **18.** $P(-3, -1), Q(5, -7)$ **19.** $P(-5, -3), Q(-3, -5)$

20. $P(-4, -5), Q(-1, 1)$ **21.** $P(2, 3), Q(4, -2)$ **22.** $P(4, 2), Q(3, 0)$

© 23. Think About a Plan An airplane at $T(80, 20)$ needs to fly to both $U(20, 60)$ and $V(110, 85)$. What is the shortest possible distance for the trip? Explain.
- What type of information do you need to find the shortest distance?
- How can you use a diagram to help you?

© 24. Reasoning The midpoint of $\overline{TS}$ is the origin. Point *T* is located in Quadrant II. What Quadrant contains point *S*? Explain.

25. Do you use the Midpoint Formula or the Distance Formula to find the following?
  a. Given points *K* and *P*, find the distance from *K* to the midpoint of $\overline{KP}$.
  b. Given point *K* and the midpoint of $\overline{KP}$, find *KP*.

For each graph, find (a) *AB* to the nearest tenth and (b) the coordinates of the midpoint of $\overline{AB}$.

26. 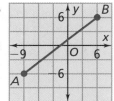   **27.** 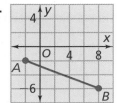   **28.**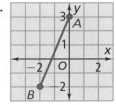

29. Coordinate Geometry Graph the points $A(2, 1), B(6, -1), C(8, 7)$, and $D(4, 9)$. Draw parallelogram *ABCD*, and diagonals $\overline{AC}$ and $\overline{BD}$.
  a. Find the midpoints of $\overline{AC}$ and $\overline{BD}$.
  b. What appears to be true about the diagonals of a parallelogram?

Travel The units of the subway map at the right are in miles. Suppose the routes between stations are straight. Find the distance you would travel between each pair of stations to the nearest tenth of a mile.

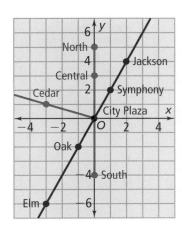

30. Oak Station and Jackson Station

31. Central Station and South Station

32. Elm Station and Symphony Station

33. Cedar Station and City Plaza Station

34. Maple Station is located 6 mi west and 2 mi north of City Plaza. What is the distance between Cedar Station and Maple Station?

35. Open-Ended Point $H(2, 2)$ is the midpoint of many segments.
- **a.** Find the coordinates of the endpoints of four noncollinear segments that have point H as their midpoint.
- **b.** You know that a segment with midpoint H has length 8. How many possible noncollinear segments match this description? Explain.

 **Challenge**

36. Points $P(-4, 6)$, $Q(2, 4)$, and R are collinear. One of the points is the midpoint of the segment formed by the other two points.
- **a.** What are the possible coordinates of R?
- **b.** **Reasoning** $RQ = \sqrt{160}$. Does this information affect your answer to part (a)? Explain.

Geometry in 3 Dimensions You can use three coordinates (x, y, z) to locate points in three dimensions.

37. Point P has coordinates $(6, -3, 9)$ as shown at the right. Give the coordinates of points $A, B, C, D, E, F,$ and G.

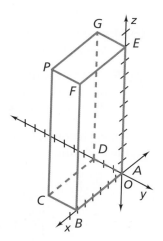

Distance in 3 Dimensions In a three-dimensional coordinate system, you can find the distance between two points (x_1, y_1, z_1) and (x_2, y_2, z_2) with this extension of the Distance Formula.

$$d = \sqrt{(x_2 - x_1)^2 + (y_2 - y_1)^2 + (z_2 - z_1)^2}$$

Find the distance between each pair of points to the nearest tenth.

38. $P(2, 3, 4)$, $Q(-2, 4, 9)$

39. $T(0, 12, 15)$, $V(-8, 20, 12)$

Quadrilaterals and Other Polygons

Prepares for **MCC9-12.G.CO.3** Given a . . . polygon, describe the rotations and reflections that carry it onto itself. Also prepares for **MCC9-12.G.GPE.7**

A **polygon** is a closed plane figure formed by three or more segments. A **quadrilateral** is a polygon with four sides. The table below shows several different types of quadrilaterals. Matching arrowheads on segments indicate parallel sides.

Definition	Example
A **parallelogram** is a quadrilateral with both pairs of opposite sides parallel.	
A **trapezoid** is a quadrilateral with exactly one pair of parallel sides, called the *bases*. The nonparallel sides are called the *legs* of the trapezoid.	
An **isosceles trapezoid** is a trapezoid with legs that are congruent.	
A **kite** is a quadrilateral with two pairs of consecutive sides congruent and no opposite sides congruent.	
A **rhombus** is a parallelogram with four congruent sides.	
A **rectangle** is a parallelogram with four right angles.	
A **square** is a parallelogram with four congruent sides and four right angles.	

Example 1

Determine the most precise name for each quadrilateral.

A

This quadrilateral is an isosceles trapezoid because it has one pair of parallel sides and one pair of opposite sides congruent.

B

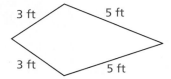

This quadrilateral is a kite because it has two pairs of consecutive sides congruent, and opposite sides are not congruent.

A polygon can be classified by its number of sides, as shown in the table below. A **regular polygon** is a polygon whose sides are all congruent and whose angles are all congruent.

Number of Sides	Name of Polygon
3	triangle
4	quadrilateral
5	pentagon
6	hexagon

Number of Sides	Name of Polygon
7	heptagon
8	octagon
9	nonagon
10	decagon

Example 2

Classify each polygon by its number of sides and by its angles.

A

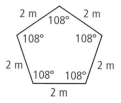

B

A This polygon has 5 sides, so it is a pentagon. Its sides are congruent and its angles are congruent, so it is a regular pentagon.

B This polygon has 8 sides, so it is an octagon. Neither its sides nor its angles are congruent, so it is not a regular octagon.

You can also classify a polygon as concave or convex, using the diagonals of the polygon. A **diagonal** is a segment that connects two nonconsecutive vertices.

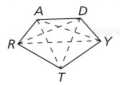

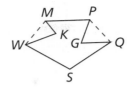

A **convex polygon** has no diagonal with points outside the polygon.

A **concave polygon** has at least one diagonal with points outside the polygon.

In this textbook, a polygon is convex unless otherwise stated.

Example 3

Tell whether the hexagon is *convex* or *concave*.

No diagonal of the hexagon contains points outside the hexagon. The hexagon is convex.

Exercises

The diagram shows the hierarchy of quadrilaterals. The arrows indicate a more specific classification. Fill in the blanks to complete the diagram.

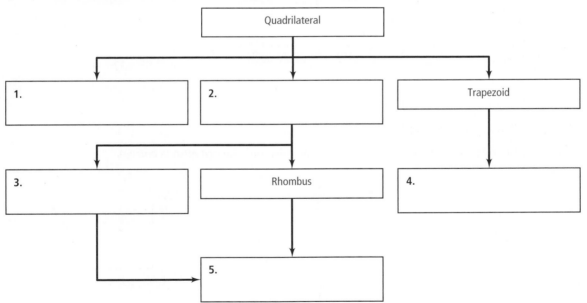

Determine the most precise name for each quadrilateral.

6. 4 in. 4 in. 4 in. 4 in.

7.

Ⓒ **8. Reasoning** Use the diagram on the previous page to determine whether a square is *sometimes*, *always*, or *never* a rhombus.

Classify each polygon by its number of sides and its angles.

9.

10.

Classify the polygon by its number of sides. Tell whether the polygon is *convex* or *concave*.

11.

12.

13.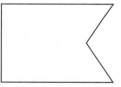

MathXL® for School
Go to pearsonsuccessnet.com

7-1 Nets and Drawings for Visualizing Geometry

Quick Review

A **net** is a two-dimensional pattern that you can fold to form a three-dimensional figure. A net shows all surfaces of a figure in one view.

An **isometric drawing** shows a corner view of a three-dimensional object. It allows you to see the top, front, and side of the object in one view.

An **orthographic drawing** shows three separate views of a three-dimensional object: a top view, a front view, and a right-side view.

Example

Draw a net for the solid at the right.

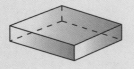

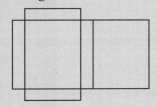

Exercises

1. The net below is for a number cube. What are the three sums of the numbers on opposite surfaces of the cube?

		5	
1	2	3	4
		6	

2. Make an orthographic drawing for the isometric drawing below. Assume there are no hidden cubes.

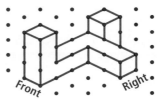

7-2 Points, Lines, and Planes

Quick Review

A **point** indicates a location and has no size.

A **line** is represented by a straight path that extends in two opposite directions without end and has no thickness.

A **plane** is represented by a flat surface that extends without end and has no thickness.

Points that lie on the same line are **collinear points**.

Points and lines in the same plane are **coplanar**.

Segments and **rays** are parts of lines.

Example

Name all the segments and rays in the figure.

Segments: $\overline{AB}$, $\overline{AC}$, $\overline{BC}$, and $\overline{BD}$

Rays: $\overrightarrow{BA}$, $\overrightarrow{CA}$ or $\overrightarrow{CB}$, $\overrightarrow{AC}$ or $\overrightarrow{AB}$, $\overrightarrow{BC}$, and $\overrightarrow{BD}$

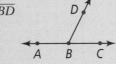

Exercises

Use the figure below for Exercises 3–5.

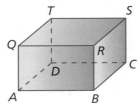

3. Name two intersecting lines.

4. Name the intersection of planes *QRBA* and *TSRQ*.

5. Name three noncollinear points.

Determine whether the statement is *true* or *false*. Explain your reasoning.

6. Two points are always collinear.

7. $\overrightarrow{LM}$ and $\overrightarrow{ML}$ are the same ray.

7-3 Measuring Segments

Quick Review

The **distance** between two points is the length of the segment connecting those points. Segments with the same length are **congruent segments**. A **midpoint** of a segment divides the segment into two congruent segments.

Example

Are $\overline{AB}$ and $\overline{CD}$ congruent?

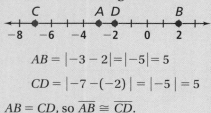

$$AB = |-3 - 2| = |-5| = 5$$

$$CD = |-7 - (-2)| = |-5| = 5$$

$AB = CD$, so $\overline{AB} \cong \overline{CD}$.

Exercises

For Exercises 8 and 9, use the number line below.

8. Find two possible coordinates of Q such that $PQ = 5$.

9. Find the coordinate of the midpoint of $\overline{PH}$.

10. Find the value of m.

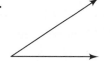

11. If $XZ = 50$, what are XY and YZ?

7-4 Measuring Angles

Quick Review

Two rays with the same endpoint form an **angle**. The endpoint is the **vertex** of the angle. You can classify angles as acute, right, obtuse, or straight. Angles with the same measure are **congruent angles**.

Example

If $m\angle AOB = 47$ and $m\angle BOC = 73$, find $m\angle AOC$.

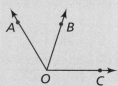

$$m\angle AOC = m\angle AOB + m\angle BOC = 47 + 73 = 120$$

Exercises

Classify each angle as acute, right, obtuse, or straight.

12.

13.

Use the diagram below for Exercises 14 and 15.

14. If $m\angle MQR = 61$ and $m\angle MQP = 25$, find $m\angle PQR$.

15. If $m\angle NQM = 2x + 8$ and $m\angle PQR = x + 22$, find the value of x.

7-5 Exploring Angle Pairs

Quick Review

Some pairs of angles have special names.

- **Adjacent angles:** coplanar angles with a common side, a common vertex, and no common interior points
- **Vertical angles:** sides are opposite rays
- **Complementary angles:** measures have a sum of 90
- **Supplementary angles:** measures have a sum of 180
- **Linear pair:** adjacent angles with noncommon sides as opposite rays

Angles of a linear pair are supplementary.

Example

Are ∠ACE and ∠BCD vertical angles? Explain.

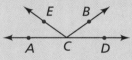

No. They have only one set of sides with opposite rays.

Exercises

Name a pair of each of the following.

16. complementary angles
17. supplementary angles
18. vertical angles
19. linear pair

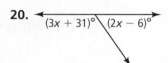

Find the value of x.

20.

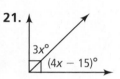

$(3x + 31)°$ $(2x - 6)°$

21.

$3x°$
$(4x - 15)°$

7-6 Midpoint and Distance in the Coordinate Plane

Quick Review

You can find the coordinates of the midpoint M of $\overline{AB}$ with endpoints $A(x_1, y_1)$ and $B(x_2, y_2)$ using the **Midpoint Formula**.

$$M\left(\frac{x_1 + x_2}{2}, \frac{y_1 + y_2}{2}\right)$$

You can find the distance d between two points $A(x_1, y_1)$ and $B(x_2, y_2)$ using the **Distance Formula**.

$$d = \sqrt{(x_2 - x_1)^2 + (y_2 - y_1)^2}$$

Example

$\overline{GH}$ has endpoints $G(-11, 6)$ and $H(3, 4)$. What are the coordinates of its midpoint M?

$$x\text{-coordinate} = \frac{-11 + 3}{2} = -4$$

$$y\text{-coordinate} = \frac{6 + 4}{2} = 5$$

The coordinates of the midpoint of $\overline{GH}$ are $M(-4, 5)$.

Exercises

Find the distance between the points to the nearest tenth.

22. $A(-1, 5), B(0, 4)$
23. $C(-1, -1), D(6, 2)$
24. $E(-7, 0), F(5, 8)$

$\overline{AB}$ **has endpoints** $A(-3, 2)$ **and** $B(3, -2)$.

25. Find the coordinates of the midpoint of $\overline{AB}$.
26. Find AB to the nearest tenth.

M **is the midpoint of** $\overline{JK}$. **Find the coordinates of** K.

27. $J(-8, 4), M(-1, 1)$
28. $J(9, -5), M(5, -2)$
29. $J(0, 11), M(-3, 2)$

Solving a Riddle

While browsing in an antique store, Cameron found a sheet of paper that came from an old book of riddles. The page is shown below.

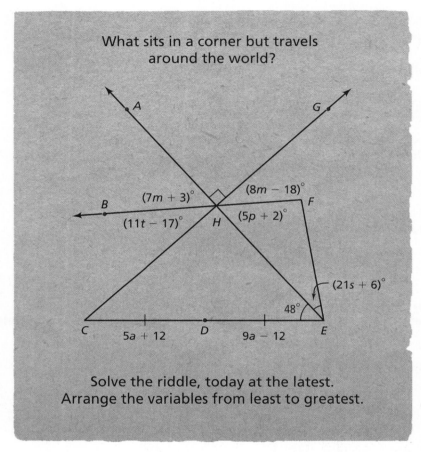

Task Description

Find the answer to the riddle.

- What segment and angle relationships are shown in the figure? How can you use these to write equations?

- Which variables can you solve for immediately, and which ones depend upon knowing the values of other variables?

Get Ready!

Identifying Polygons

Identify each polygon.

1. a polygon with 5 sides

2. a polygon with 10 congruent angles and 10 congruent sides

3. a parallelogram with 4 congruent sides

4. a parallelogram with 4 right angles

5. a quadrilateral with exactly 2 parallel sides

Translating Graphs

Describe how each function is a translation of the parent function $y = |x|$.

6. $g(x) = |x| + 4$

7. $h(x) = |x + 1| - 2$

8. $j(x) = |x - 5| + 1$

Writing a Function Rule

Write a function rule for each situation.

9. the area A of a rectangle when you know the length ℓ is 7 ft more than the width w

10. the cost C to buy p pounds of pasta at \$1.29 per lb

11. the perimeter P of a rectangular garden whose width w is 3 ft less than its length ℓ

 Looking Ahead Vocabulary

12. Think about your *reflection* in a mirror. If you raise your right hand, which hand appears to be raised in your *reflection*? If you are standing 2 ft from the mirror, how far away from you does your *reflection* appear to be?

13. The minute hand of a clock *rotates* as the minutes go by. What point of the minute hand stays fixed as the hand *rotates*?

Transformations

Big Ideas

1 Transformations
Essential Question How can you change a figure's position without changing its size and shape?

2 Coordinate Geometry
Essential Question How can you represent a transformation in the coordinate plane?

©Domain

• Congruence

Chapter Preview

8-1 Translations
8-2 Reflections
8-3 Rotations
8-4 Compositions of Isometries

Interactive Digital Path

Log in to **pearsonsuccessnet.com** and click on Interactive Digital Path to access the Solve Its and animated Problems.

Vocabulary

English/Spanish Vocabulary Audio Online:

English	Spanish
image, *p. 495*	imagen
isometry, *p. 532*	isometría
preimage, *p. 495*	preimagen
reflection, *p. 508*	reflexión
rigid motion, *p. 495*	movimiento rígido
rotation, *p. 515*	rotación
translation, *p. 498*	traslación

Tracing Paper Transformations

MCC9-12.G.CO.2 Represent transformations in the plane . . .

In this activity, you will use tracing paper to perform translations, rotations, and reflections.

Activity

Step 1 Copy △*ABC* and the *x*- and *y*-axis on graph paper. Trace the copy of △*ABC* on tracing paper.

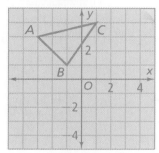

Step 2 Translate △*ABC* up 4 units and to the right 2 units by sliding the tracing paper. Draw the new triangle on the graph paper and label it △*A′B′C′* so that the original vertices *A*, *B*, and *C* correspond to the vertices *A′*, *B′*, and *C′* of the new triangle. What are the coordinates of the vertices of △*A′B′C′*? What is the same about the triangles? What is different?

Step 3 Align your tracing of △*ABC* with the original and then trace the positive *x*-axis and the origin.

Step 4 Rotate △*ABC* 90° counterclockwise about the origin by keeping the origin in place and aligning the traced axis with the positive *y*-axis. You can use the point of your pencil to hold the origin in place as you rotate the triangle. Draw the image of △*ABC* after the rotation on the graph paper and label it △*A″B″C″*. Compare the coordinates of the vertices of △*ABC* with the coordinates of the vertices of △*A″B″C″*. Describe the pattern.

Step 5 Flip your tracing of △*ABC* over and align the origin and the traced positive *x*-axis to reflect △*ABC* across the *x*-axis. Draw and label the reflected triangle △*A‴B‴C‴* on the graph paper. What do you notice about the orientations of the triangles?

In Exercises 1 and 2 on the next page, you will find the images of other triangles after translating, rotating, and reflecting.

Exercises

Use tracing paper. Find the images of each triangle for a translation 3 units left and 5 units down, a 90° rotation counterclockwise about the origin, and a reflection across the *x*-axis.

1.
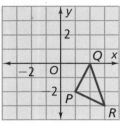

translation

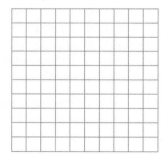

rotation

reflection

2.
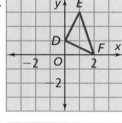

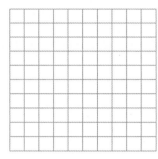

translation

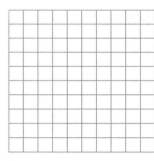

rotation

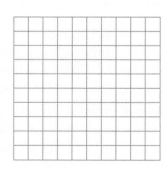

reflection

8-1 Translations

MCC9-12.G.CO.5 Given a geometric figure and a . . . translation, draw the transformed figure . . . Specify a sequence of transformations that will carry a given figure onto another. Also **MCC9-12.G.CO.2, MCC9-12.G.CO.4**

Objectives To identify rigid motions
To find translation images of figures

Solve It! Write your solution to the Solve It in the space below.

In the Solve It, you described changes in positions of letters. In this lesson, you will learn some of the mathematical language used to describe changes in positions of geometric figures.

Essential Understanding You can change the position of a geometric figure so that the angle measures and the distance between any two points of a figure stay the same.

A **transformation** of a geometric figure is a function, or *mapping,* that results in a change in the position, shape, or size of the figure. When you play dominoes, you often move the dominoes by flipping them, sliding them, or turning them. Each move is a type of transformation. The diagrams below illustrate some basic transformations that you will study.

The domino flips.   The domino slides.   The domino turns.

In a transformation, the original figure is the **preimage**. The resulting figure is the **image**. Some transformations, like those shown by the dominoes, preserve distance and angle measures. To preserve distance means that the distance between any two points of the image is the same as the distance between the corresponding points of the preimage. To preserve angles means that the angles of the image have the same angle measure as the corresponding angles of the preimage. A transformation that preserves distance and angle measures is called a **rigid motion**.

Problem 1 Identifying a Rigid Motion

Got It? Does the transformation appear to be a rigid motion? Explain.

a.

Preimage Image

b.

Image

Preimage

ⒶPractice Tell whether the transformation appears to be a rigid motion. Explain.

1.

Image

Preimage

2.

Preimage Image

A transformation maps every point of a figure onto its image and may be described with arrow notation (→). Prime notation (′) is sometimes used to identify image points. In the diagram below, K' is the image of K.

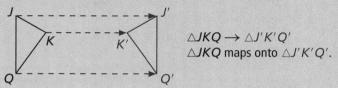

$\triangle JKQ \rightarrow \triangle J'K'Q'$
$\triangle JKQ$ maps onto $\triangle J'K'Q'$.

Notice that you list corresponding points of the preimage and image in the same order.

 Problem 2   **Naming Images and Corresponding Parts**

Got It?   In the diagram, $\triangle NID \rightarrow \triangle SUP$.

a. What are the images of $\angle I$ and point D?

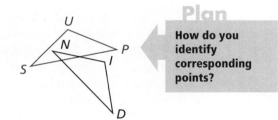

> **Plan**
>
> **How do you identify corresponding points?**

b. What are the pairs of corresponding sides?

 Practice   In each diagram, the red figure is an image of the blue figure.
(a) Choose an angle or point from the preimage and name its image.
(b) List all pairs of corresponding sides.

3.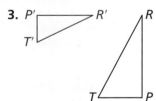

4.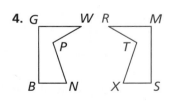

Key Concept Translation

A **translation** is a transformation that maps all points of a figure the
same distance in the same direction.

You write the translation that maps $\triangle ABC$ onto $\triangle A'B'C'$ as
$T(\triangle ABC) = \triangle A'B'C'$. A translation is a rigid motion with the
following properties.

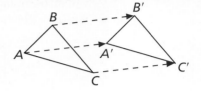

If $T(\triangle ABC) = \triangle A'B'C'$, then
- $AA' = BB' = CC'$
- $AB = A'B', BC = B'C', AC = A'C'$
- $m\angle A = m\angle A', m\angle B = m\angle B', m\angle C = m\angle C'$

The diagram at the right shows a
translation in the coordinate plane.
Each point of $ABCD$ is translated 4 units
right and 2 units down. So each (x, y) pair
in $ABCD$ is mapped to $(x + 4, y - 2)$. You
can use the function notation
$T_{<4, -2>}(ABCD) = A'B'C'D'$ to describe this
translation, where 4 represents the translation of each point of the figure 4 units right
and -2 represents the translation 2 units down.

> B moves 4 units
> right and
> 2 units down.

Problem 3 Finding the Image of a Translation

Got It? **a.** What are the vertices of $T_{<1,-4>}(\triangle ABC)$? Copy $\triangle ABC$ and
graph its image.

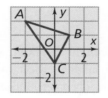

Think

What does
the rule tell
you about the
direction each
point moves?

b. Reasoning Draw $\overline{AA'}$, $\overline{BB'}$, and $\overline{CC'}$. What relationships exist among
these three segments? How do you know?

A Practice Copy each graph. Graph the image of each figure under the given translation.

5. $T_{<5, -1>}(x, y)$

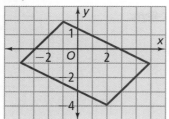

6. $T_{<-2, 5>}(x, y)$

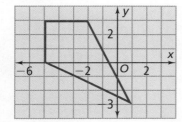

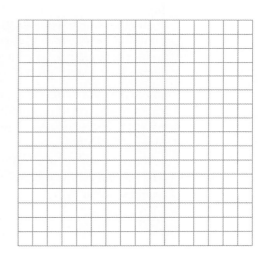

Problem 4 Writing a Rule to Describe a Translation

Got It? The translation image of $\triangle LMN$ is $\triangle L'M'N'$ with L' (1,−2), M' (3,−4), and N' (6,−2). What is a rule that describes the translation?

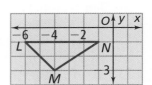

A Practice The red figure is a translation image of the blue figure. Write a rule to describe each translation.

7.
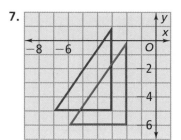

8.
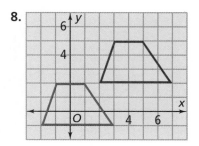

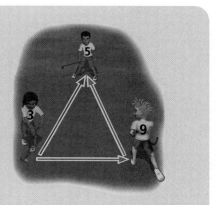

A **composition of transformations** is a combination of two or more transformations. In a composition, you perform each transformation on the image of the preceding transformation.

In the diagram at the right, the field hockey ball can move from Player 3 to Player 5 by a direct pass. This translation is represented by the blue arrow. The ball can also be passed from Player 3 to Player 9, and then from Player 9 to Player 5. The two red arrows represent this composition of translations.

In general, the composition of any two translations is another translation.

Problem 5 **Composing Translations**

Got It? In Problem 5, the bishop next moves 3 squares left and 3 squares down. Where is the bishop in relation to its original position?

Practice

9. Travel You are visiting San Francisco. From your hotel near Union Square, you walk 4 blocks east and 4 blocks north to the Wells Fargo History Museum. Then you walk 5 blocks west and 3 blocks north to the Cable Car Barn Museum. Where is the Cable Car Barn Museum in relation to your hotel?

10. Travel Your friend and her parents are visiting colleges. They leave their home in Enid, Oklahoma, and drive to Tulsa, which is 107 mi east and 18 mi south of Enid. From Tulsa, they go to Norman, 83 mi west and 63 mi south of Tulsa. Where is Norman in relation to Enid?

 Lesson Check

Do you know HOW?

11. If $\triangle JPT \rightarrow \triangle J'P'T'$, what are the images of P and $\overline{TJ}$?

12. Graph $T_{<-3,\,-4>}(NILE)$.

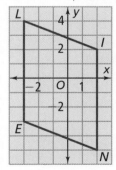

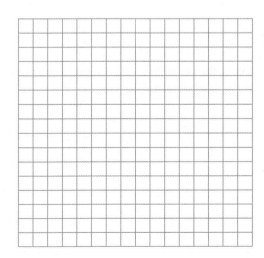

13. Point $H(x, y)$ moves 12 units left and 4 units up. What is a rule that describes this translation?

Do you UNDERSTAND?

@ 14. Vocabulary What is true about a transformation that is not a rigid motion? Include a sketch of an example.

@ 15. Error Analysis Your friend says the transformation $\triangle ABC \rightarrow \triangle PQR$ is a translation. Explain and correct her error.

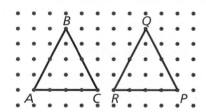

@ 16. Reasoning Write the translation $T_{\langle 1, -3 \rangle}(x, y)$ as a composition of a horizontal translation and a vertical translation.

 Apply

17. In the diagram at the right, the red figure is a translation image of the blue figure. Write a rule that describes the translation.

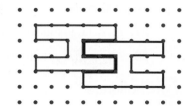

18. Think About a Plan $\triangle MUG$ has coordinates $M(2, -4)$, $U(6, 6)$, and $G(7, 2)$. A translation maps point M to $M'(-3, 6)$. What are the coordinates of U' and G' for this translation?
  • How can you use a graph to help you visualize the problem?
  • How can you find a rule that describes the translation?

Geometry in 3 Dimensions Follow the sample below. Use each figure, graph paper, and the given translation to draw a three-dimensional figure.

SAMPLE Use the rectangle and the translation $T_{<3, 1>}(x, y)$ to draw a box.

Step 1

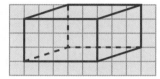

Step 2

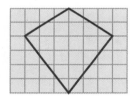

19. $T_{<2, -1>}(x, y)$

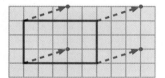

20. $T_{<-2, 2>}(x, y)$

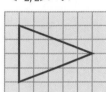

21. $T_{<-3, -5>}(x, y)$

22. Open-Ended You are a graphic designer for a company that manufactures wrapping paper. Make a design for wrapping paper that involves translations.

23. Reasoning If $T_{<5, 7>}(\triangle MNO) = \triangle M'N'O'$, what translation rule maps $\triangle M'N'O'$ onto $\triangle MNO$?

24. Landscaping The diagram at the right shows the site plan for a backyard storage shed. Local law, however, requires the shed to sit at least 15 ft from property lines. Describe how to move the shed to comply with the law.

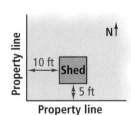

STEM 25. Computer Animation You write a computer animation program to help young children learn the alphabet. The program draws a letter, erases the letter, and makes it reappear in a new location two times. The program uses the following composition of translations to move the letter.

$$T_{<5, 7>}(x, y) \text{ followed by } T_{<-9, -2>}(x, y)$$

Suppose the program makes the letter W by connecting the points $(1, 2)$, $(2, 0)$, $(3, 2)$, $(4, 0)$, and $(5, 2)$. What points does the program connect to make the last W?

26. Use the graph at the right. Write three different translation rules for which the image of $\triangle JKL$ has a vertex at the origin.

Find a translation that has the same effect as each composition of translations.

27. $T_{<2,\,5>}(x, y)$ followed by $T_{<-4,\,9>}(x, y)$

28. $T_{<12,\,0.5>}(x, y)$ followed by $T_{<1,\,-3>}(x, y)$

Ⓒ Challenge

29. Coordinate Geometry $\triangle ABC$ has vertices $A(-2, 5)$, $B(-4, -1)$, and $C(2, -3)$. If $T_{<4,\,2>}(\triangle ABC) = \triangle A'B'C'$, show that the images of the midpoints of the sides of $\triangle ABC$ are the midpoints of the sides of $\triangle A'B'C'$.

Ⓖ **30. Writing** Explain how to use translations to draw a parallelogram.

Paper Folding and Reflections

MCC9-12.G.CO.5 Given a geometric figure and a . . . reflection . . . , draw the transformed figure . . .

In Activity 1, you will see how a figure and its *reflection* image are related. In Activity 2, you will use these relationships to construct a reflection image.

Activity 1

Step 1 Use a piece of tracing paper and a straightedge. Using less than half the page, draw a large, scalene triangle. Label its vertices *A*, *B*, and *C*.

Step 2 Fold the paper so that your triangle is covered. Trace △*ABC* using a straightedge.

Step 3 Unfold the paper. Label the traced points corresponding to *A*, *B*, and *C* as *A*′ , *B*′ , and *C*′, respectively. △*A*′*B*′*C*′ is a reflection image of △*ABC*. The fold is the reflection line.

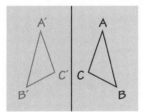 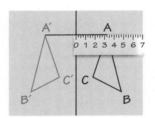

1. Use a ruler to draw $\overline{AA'}$. Measure the perpendicular distances from *A* to the fold and from *A*′ to the fold. What do you notice?

2. Measure the angles formed by the fold and $\overline{AA'}$. What are the angle measures?

3. Repeat Exercises 1 and 2 for B and B' and for C and C'. Then, make a conjecture: How is the reflection line related to the segment joining a point and its image?

Activity 2

Step 1   On regular paper, draw a simple shape or design made of segments. Use less than half the page. Draw a reflection line near your figure.

Step 2   Draw a line perpendicular to the reflection line through one point of your drawing.

4. Explain how you can use a ruler and the perpendicular you drew to find the reflection image of the point you chose.

5. Connect the reflection images for several points of your shape and complete the image. Check the accuracy of the reflection image by folding the paper along the reflection line and holding it up to a light source.

8-2 Reflections

MCC9-12.G.CO.5 Given a geometric figure and a rotation . . . draw the transformed figure . . . Specify a sequence of transformations that will carry a given figure onto another. Also **MCC9-12.G.CO.2, MCC9-12.G.CO.4**

Objective To find reflection images of figures

Solve It! Write your solution to the Solve It in the space below.

In the Solve It, you reflected shapes across lines. Notice that when you reflect a figure, the shapes have *opposite orientations*. Two figures have opposite orientations if the corresponding vertices of the preimage and image read in opposite directions.

The vertices of △*BUG* read clockwise.

The vertices of △*B′U′G′* read counterclockwise.

Essential Understanding When you reflect a figure across a line, each point of the figure maps to another point the same distance from the line but on the other side. The orientation of the figure reverses.

In order to precisely define reflections, you need to use the *perpendicular bisector* of a segment, which is the line perpendicular to the segment at its midpoint. A point (or line) is *equidistant* from a set of other points when it is the same distance from each of those other points.

A **reflection** across a line m, called the **line of reflection**, is a transformation with the following properties:
- If a point A is on line m, then the image of A is itself (that is, $A' = A$).
- If a point B is not on line m, then m is the perpendicular bisector of $\overline{BB'}$.

You write the reflection across m that takes P to P' as $R_m(P) = P'$.

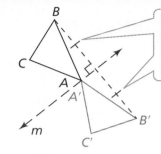

The preimage B and its image B' are equidistant from the line of reflection.

You can use the equation of a line of reflection in the function notation. For example, $R_{y=x}$ describes the reflection across the line $y = x$.

Problem 1   **Reflecting a Point Across a Line**

Got It?   Point P has coordinates $(3, 4)$. If $R_{x=1}(P) = P'$, what are the coordinates of P'?

Think

How does a graph help you visualize the problem?

Ⓐ Practice   Find the coordinates of each image.

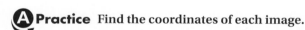

1. $R_{x=-3}(U)$

2. $R_{x\text{-axis}}(V)$

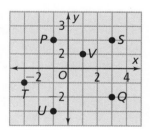

You can also use the notation R_m to describe reflections of figures. The diagram on the next page shows $R_m(\triangle ABC)$, and function notation is used to describe some of the properties of reflections.

Property Properties of Reflections

- Reflections preserve distance.
  If $R_m(A) = A'$, and $R_m(B) = B'$, then $AB = A'B'$.
- Reflections preserve angle measure.
  If $R_m(\angle ABC) = \angle A'B'C'$, then $m\angle ABC = m\angle A'B'C'$.
- Reflections map each point of the preimage to one and only one corresponding point of its image.
  $R_m(A) = A'$ if and only if $R_m(A') = A$.

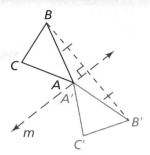

Observe that the above properties mean that reflections are rigid motions, which you learned about in Lesson 8-1.

 Problem 2 **Graphing a Reflection Image**

Got It? Graph $\triangle ABC$ from Problem 2. Graph and label $R_{x\text{-axis}}(\triangle ABC)$.

Practice **Coordinate Geometry** Given points $J(1, 4)$, $A(3, 5)$, and $G(2, 1)$, graph $\triangle JAG$ and its reflection image as indicated.

3. $R_{y=5}$

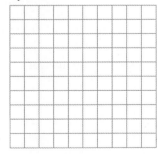

4. $R_{x=2}$

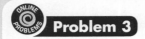
Got It?   Use the figure in Problem 3. How can you use a reflection rule to describe Triangle 1? Explain.

 Practice   **5.** Each figure in the diagram at the right is a reflection of another figure across one of the reflection lines.

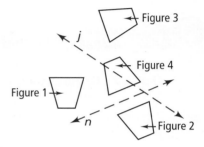

   a. Write a reflection rule to describe Figure 3. Justify your answer.

   b. Write a reflection rule to describe Figure 2. Justify your answer.

   c. Write a reflection rule to describe Figure 4. Justify your answer.

You can use the properties of reflections to prove statements about figures.

 Problem 4 **Using Properties of Reflections**

Got It? Can you use properties of reflections to prove that $\triangle GHJ$ is equilateral? Explain.

Think

What do you need to prove to show that $\triangle GHJ$ is equilateral?

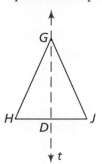

ⒶPractice **6.** In the diagram below, *LMNP* is a rectangle with $LM = 2MN$.

 a. Sketch $R_{\overline{LM}}(LMNP)$.

 b. What figure results from the reflection? Use properties of reflections to justify your solution.

Lesson Check

Do you know HOW?

Use the graph of $\triangle FGH$.

7. What are the coordinates of $R_{y\text{-axis}}(H)$?

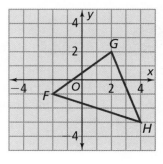

8. What are the coordinates of $R_{x=3}(G)$?

9. Graph and label $R_{y=4}(\triangle FGH)$.

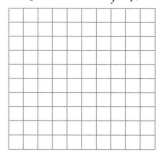

Do you UNDERSTAND?

MATHEMATICAL
PRACTICES

10. Vocabulary What is the relationship between a line of reflection and a segment joining corresponding points of the preimage and image?

11. Error Analysis A classmate sketched $R_s(A) = A'$ as shown in the diagram.

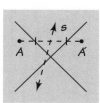

  a. Explain your classmate's error.

  b. Copy point A and line s and show the correct location of A'.

12. What are the coordinates of a point $P(x, y)$ reflected across the y-axis? Across the x-axis? Use reflection notation to write your answer.

More Practice and Problem-Solving Exercises

B Apply

Copy each figure and line ℓ. Draw each figure's reflection image across line ℓ.

13.

14.

15. Think About a Plan The coordinates of the vertices of $\triangle FGH$ are $F(2, -1)$, $G(-2, -2)$, and $H(-4, 3)$. Graph $\triangle FGH$ and $R_{y=x-3}(\triangle FGH)$.
 • What is the relationship between the line $y = x - 3$ and $\overline{FF'}$, $\overline{GG'}$ and $\overline{HH'}$?
 • How can you use slope to find the image of each vertex?

16. In the diagram $R(ABCDE) = A'B'C'D'E'$.
 a. What are the midpoints of $\overline{AA'}$ and $\overline{DD'}$?
 b. What is the equation of the line of reflection?
 c. Write a rule that describes this reflection.

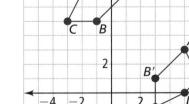

Copy each pair of figures. Then draw the line of reflection you can use to map one figure onto the other.

17.

18.

19. **History** The work of artist and scientist Leonardo da Vinci (1452–1519) has an unusual characteristic. His handwriting is a mirror image of normal handwriting.

   a. Write the mirror image of the sentence, "Leonardo da Vinci was left-handed." Use a mirror to check how well you did.

   b. Explain why the fact about da Vinci in part (a) might have made mirror writing seem natural to him.

© 20. **Open-Ended** Give three examples from everyday life of objects or situations that show or use reflections.

Find the image of $O(0, 0)$ after two reflections, first across line ℓ_1 and then across line ℓ_2.

21. $\ell_1: y = 3, \ell_2: x$-axis   22. $\ell_1: x = -2, \ell_2: y$-axis   23. $\ell_1: x$-axis, $\ell_2: y$-axis

© 24. **Reasoning** When you reflect a figure across a line, does every point on the preimage move the same distance? Explain.

25. Use the diagram at the right. Find the coordinates of each image point.

   a. $R_{y=x}(A) = A'$

   b. $R_{y=-x}(A') = A''$

   c. $R_{y=x}(A'') = A'''$

   d. $R_{y=-x}(A''') = A''''$

   e. How are A and A'''' related?

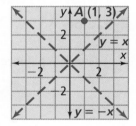

© Challenge

© **Reasoning** Can you form the given type of quadrilateral by drawing a triangle and then reflecting one or more times? Explain.

26. parallelogram   27. isosceles trapezoid   28. kite

29. rhombus   30. rectangle   31. square

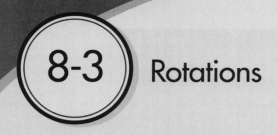

8-3 Rotations

MCC9-12.G.CO.4 Develop definitions of rotations . . . in terms of angles, circles, perpendicular lines, . . . and line segments. Also MCC9-12.G.CO.2, MCC9-12.G.CO.5

Objective To draw and identify rotation images of figures

Solve It! Write your solution to the Solve It in the space below.

In the Solve It, you thought about how the coordinates of a point change as it turns, or *rotates*, about the origin on a coordinate grid. In this lesson, you will learn how to recognize and draw rotations of geometric figures.

Essential Understanding Rotations preserve distance, angle measures, and orientation of figures.

take note

Key Concept Rotation About a Point

A **rotation** of $x°$ about a point Q, called the **center of rotation**, is a transformation with these two properties:

- The image of Q is itself (that is, $Q' = Q$).
- For any other point V, $QV' = QV$ and $m\angle VQV' = x$.

The number of degrees a figure rotates is the **angle of rotation**.

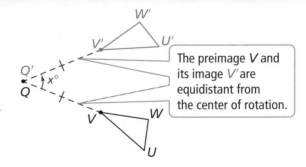

The preimage V and its image V' are equidistant from the center of rotation.

A rotation about a point is a rigid motion. You write the $x°$ rotation of $\triangle UVW$ about point Q as $r_{(x°,\, Q)}(\triangle UVW) = \triangle U'V'W'$.

Unless stated otherwise, rotations in this book are counterclockwise.

Got It? Copy △*LOB* from Problem 1. What is the image of △*LOB* for a 50° rotation about *B*?

Ⓐ Practice Draw the image of each figure for the given rotation about *P*. Use prime notation to label the vertices of the image.

1. 60°

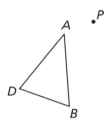

2. 90°

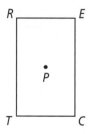

When a figure is rotated 90°, 180°, 270°, or 360° about the origin O in a coordinate plane, you can use the following rules.

Key Concept   Rotation in the Coordinate Plane

$r_{(90°, O)}(x, y) = (-y, x)$

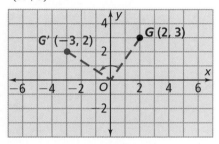

$r_{(180°, O)}(x, y) = (-x, -y)$

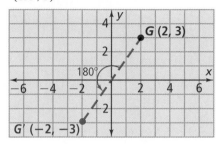

$r_{(270°, O)}(x, y) = (y, -x)$

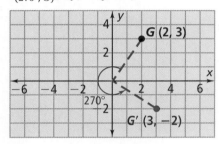

$r_{(360°, O)}(x, y) = (x, y)$

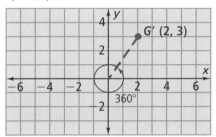

Problem 2   **Drawing Rotations in a Coordinate Plane**

Got It?   Graph $r_{(270°, O)}(FGHI)$.

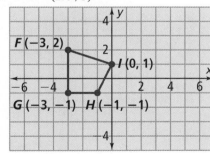

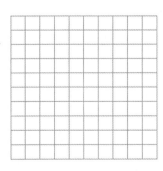

Plan

How do you know where to draw the vertices on the coordinate plane?

Practice For Exercises 3 and 4, use the graph at the right.

3. Graph $r_{(90°,\ O)}(FGHJ)$.

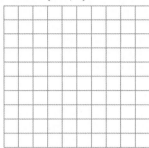

4. Graph $r_{(270°,\ O)}(FGHJ)$.

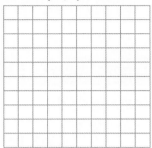

You can use the properties of rotations to solve problems.

 Problem 3 **Using Properties of Rotations**

Got It? Use the figure in Problem 3. Can you use the properties of rotations to prove that *WXYZ* is a rhombus? Explain.

Plan

What would you need to show that *WXYZ* is a rhombus?

Practice For Exercises 5 and 6, use the diagram at the right. *TQNV* is a rectangle. *M* is the midpoint of the diagonals.

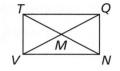

    5. Use the properties of rotations to show that the measures of both pairs of opposite sides are equal in length.

    Ⓒ **6. Reasoning** Can you use the properties of rotations to show that the measures of the lengths of the diagonals are equal?

 ## Lesson Check

Do you know HOW?

    7. Draw $r_{(70°,\, P)}(\triangle ABC)$.

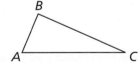

In the figure at the right, point A is equidistant from the vertices of square $SQRE$.

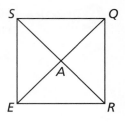

8. What is $r_{(90°, A)}(E)$?

9. What is the image of $\overline{RQ}$ for a 180° rotation about A?

10. Use the properties of rotations to describe how you know that the lengths of the diagonals of the square are equal.

Do you UNDERSTAND?

MATHEMATICAL
PRACTICES

11. Vocabulary $\triangle A'B'C'$ is a rotation image of $\triangle ABC$ about point O. Describe how to find the angle of rotation.

12. Error Analysis A classmate drew a 115° rotation of $\triangle PQR$ about point P, as shown at the right. Explain and correct your classmate's error.

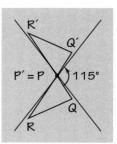

© 13. **Compare and Contrast** Compare rotating a figure about a point to reflecting the figure across a line. How are the transformations alike? How are they different?

© 14. **Reasoning** Point $P(x, y)$ is rotated about the origin by 135° and then by 45°. What are the coordinates of the image of point P? Explain.

More Practice and Problem-Solving Exercises

B Apply

15. In the diagram at the right, $\overline{M'N'}$ is the rotation image of $\overline{MN}$ about point E. Name all pairs of angles and all pairs of segments that have equal measures in the diagram.

16. **Language Arts** Symbols are used in dictionaries to help users pronounce words correctly. The ə symbol is called a *schwa*. It is used in dictionaries to represent neutral vowel sounds such as *a* in *ago*, *i* in *sanity*, and *u* in *focus*. What transformation maps a ə to a lowercase e?

Find the angle of rotation about C that maps the blue figure to the red figure.

17.

18.
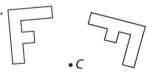

19.
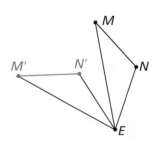

20. Think About a Plan The Millenium Wheel, also known as the London Eye, contains 32 observation cars. Determine the angle of rotation that will bring Car 3 to the position of Car 18.
  - How do you find the angle of rotation that a car travels when it moves one position counterclockwise?
  - How many positions does Car 3 move?

21. Reasoning For center of rotation *P*, does an $x°$ rotation followed by a $y°$ rotation give the same image as a $y°$ rotation followed by an $x°$ rotation? Explain.

22. Writing Describe how a series of rotations can have the same effect as a 360° rotation about a point *X*.

23. Coordinate Geometry Graph *A*(5, 2). Graph *B*, the image of *A* for a 90° rotation about the origin *O*. Graph *C*, the image of *A* for a 180° rotation about *O*. Graph *D*, the image of *A* for a 270° rotation about *O*. What type of quadrilateral is *ABCD*? Explain.

Point *O* is equidistant from the vertices of the regular nonagon shown at the right.

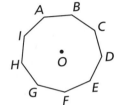

24. Find the angle of rotation that maps *F* to *H*.

25. Open-Ended Describe a rotation that maps *H* to *C*.

26. Error Analysis Your friend says that $\overline{AB}$ is the image of $\overline{ED}$ for a 120° rotation about *O*. What is wrong with your friend's statement?

In the figure at the right, the large triangle, the quadrilateral, and the hexagon are regular. Find the image of each point or segment for the given rotation or composition of rotations. (Hint: Adjacent red segments form 30° angles.)

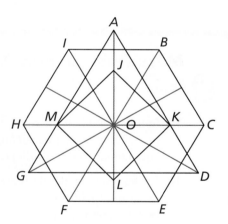

27. $r_{(120°, O)}(B)$ **28.** $r_{(270°, O)}(L)$

29. $r_{(300°, O)}(\overline{IB})$ **30.** $r_{(60°, O)}(E)$

31. $r_{(180°, O)}(\overline{JK})$ **32.** $r_{(240°, O)}(G)$

33. $r_{(120°, H)}(F)$ **34.** $r_{(270°, L)}(M)$

35. $r_{(180°, O)}(I)$ **36.** $r_{(270°, O)}(M)$

Ⓒ Challenge

37. Coordinate Geometry Draw △*LMN* with vertices *L*(2, −1), *M*(6, −2), and *N*(4, 2). Find the coordinates of the vertices after a 90° rotation about the origin and about each of the points *L*, *M*, and *N*.

38. Reasoning If you are given a figure and a rotation image of the figure, how can you find the center and angle of rotation?

Symmetry

MCC9-12.G.CO.3 Given a . . . polygon, describe the rotations and reflections that carry it onto itself.

You can use what you know about reflections and rotations to identify types of **symmetry**. A figure has symmetry if there is a rigid motion that maps the figure onto itself.

A figure has **line symmetry**, or **reflectional symmetry**, if there is a reflection for which the figure is its own image. The line of reflection is called the **line of symmetry**.

A figure has a **rotational symmetry**, if its image, after a rotation of less than 360°, is exactly the same as the original figure. A figure has **point symmetry** if a 180° rotation about a center of rotation maps the figure onto itself.

Activity 1

1. Refer to the rhombus at the right.

   a. How many lines of reflection, or lines of symmetry, does the rhombus have?

   b. Draw all of the lines of symmetry.

2. Do all parallelograms have reflectional symmetry? Explain your reasoning.

3. The isosceles trapezoid at the right has only 1 pair of parallel sides. How many lines of symmetry does the trapezoid have?

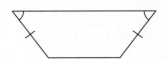

4. Do all isosceles trapezoids have reflectional symmetry? Do all trapezoids have reflectional symmetry? Explain.

Activity 2

5. Refer to the regular hexagon at the right.

    a. How many lines of symmetry does a regular hexagon have?

    b. Draw all of the lines of symmetry.

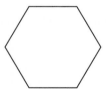

6. What are the center and angle(s) of the rotations that map the regular hexagon onto itself?

7. Do all regular polygons have rotational symmetry? Explain your reasoning.

8. Do all regular polygons have point symmetry? Explain.

Activity 3

Copy and cut out the shapes below. Shade $\frac{1}{2}$ of each square to represent the darker sections. Arrange the shapes to make a design that has both reflectional symmetry and rotational symmetry.

9. Draw the design you made.

10. How many lines of symmetry does your design have? Sketch each line of symmetry.

11. Why is the shading of the tiles important to the symmetry?

12. Does your design have more than one of angle of rotation that maps it onto itself? If so, what are they?

13. Can you change the center of rotation and still map the figure onto itself? Explain.

Exercises

Tell what type(s) of symmetry each figure has. Sketch the figure and the line(s) of symmetry, and give the angle(s) of rotation when appropriate.

14.

15.

16.

© 17. **Vocabulary** If a figure has point symmetry, must it also have rotational symmetry? Explain.

18. Writing A quadrilateral with vertices $(1, 5)$ and $(-2, -3)$ has point symmetry about the origin.

    a. How can you use point symmetry to find the other vertices?

    b. Show that the quadrilateral is a parallelogram.

19. Error Analysis Your friend thinks that the regular pentagon in the diagram has 10 lines of symmetry. Explain and correct your friend's error.

Exploring Multiple Transformations

MCC9-12.G.CO.2 Represent transformations in the plane using, e.g., . . . geometry software . . . Also **MCC9-12.G.CO.5**

**MATHEMATICAL
PRACTICES**

You can use geometry software to explore compositions of transformations.

Activity 1

Step 1 Draw △*ABC*. Construct two parallel lines that do not intersect the triangle, and label them *m* and *s*.

Step 2 Reflect △*ABC* across line *m*. Label the vertices of the reflected triangle as shown.

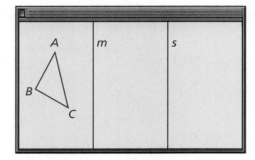

Step 3 Reflect △*DEF* across line *s*. Label the vertices of the reflected triangle as shown.

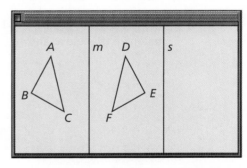

Step 4 Drag elements of the construction to different parts of the display window, including △*ABC* and lines *m* and *s*. Observe how the three triangles move relative to each other.

Activity 2

Step 1 Draw △LMN and two intersecting lines that do not intersect the triangle. Label the lines *j* and *k*.

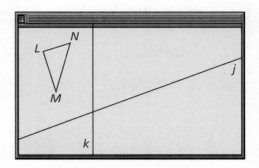

Step 2 Reflect △LMN across line *k*. Label the vertices of the reflected triangle as shown.

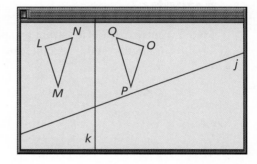

Step 3 Reflect △OPQ across line *j*. Label the vertices of the reflected triangle as shown.

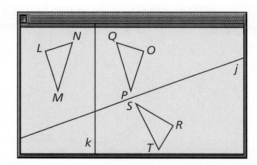

Step 4 Drag elements of the construction to different parts of the display window, including △LMN and lines *k* and *j*. Observe how the three triangles move relative to each other.

Exercises

1. **Make a Conjecture** In Activity 1, what is a single transformation that will map △*ABC* onto △*GHI*? Make a conjecture about the result of a composition of reflections of a preimage across two parallel lines.

2. In Activity 2, suppose that the intersecting lines were perpendicular. What rotation could you use to get the same result as reflecting the preimage across two perpendicular lines?

3. **Reasoning** Use geometry software to measure the side lengths and angle measures of all of the triangles in Activity 1 and in Activity 2. What can you conclude about the relationships between corresponding sides and angles of the preimage and image after a composition of transformations?

Compositions of Isometries

MCC9-12.G.CO.5 Given a geometric figure and a rotation, reflection, or translation, draw the transformed figure . . . Specify a sequence of transformations that will carry a given figure onto another. Also **MCC9-12.G.CO.2**

Objectives To find compositions of isometries, including glide reflections
To classify isometries

 Solve It! Write your solution to the Solve It in the space below.

In the Solve It, you looked for a way to use two reflections to produce the same image as a given horizontal translation. In this lesson, you will learn that any rigid motion can be expressed as a composition of reflections.

The term *isometry* means "same distance." An **isometry** is a transformation that preserves distance, or length. So, translations, reflections, and rotations are isometries.

Essential Understanding You can express all isometries as compositions of reflections.

Expressing isometries as compositions of reflections depends on the following fact.

take note

Key Concept Composition of Isometries

The composition of two or more isometries is an isometry.

There are only four kinds of isometries.

Translation	Rotation	Reflection	Glide Reflection
R ⟍ R	∝ ⤙ R	R∣Я	R ⟶ R / Я

You will learn about *glide reflections* later in the lesson.

In Lesson 8-1, you learned that a composition of transformations is a combination of two or more transformations, one performed after the other.

Key Concept   Reflections Across Parallel Lines

A composition of reflections across two parallel lines is a translation.

You can write this composition as
$(R_m \circ R_\ell)(\triangle ABC) = \triangle A''B''C''$
or $R_m(R_\ell(\triangle ABC)) = \triangle A''B''C''$.

$\overline{AA''}$, $\overline{BB''}$, and $\overline{CC''}$ are all perpendicular to lines ℓ and m.

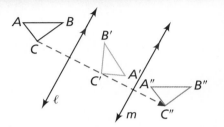

Problem 1   Composing Reflections Across Parallel Lines

Got It?   **a.** Draw parallel lines ℓ and m as in Problem 1. Draw J between ℓ and m. What is the image of $(R_m \circ R_\ell)(J)$? What is the distance of the resulting translation?

Think

Which line do you reflect over first?

b. Reasoning Use the results of part (a) and Problem 1. Make a conjecture about the distance of any translation that is the result of a composition of reflections across two parallel lines.

Practice Find the image of each letter after the transformation $R_m \circ R_\ell$.
Describe the resulting translation.

1.
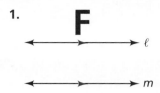

2.
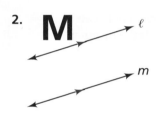

Key Concept   Reflections Across Intersecting Lines

A composition of reflections across two intersecting lines is a rotation.

You can write this composition as $(R_m \circ R_\ell)(\triangle ABC) = \triangle A''B''C''$ or
$R_m(R_\ell(\triangle ABC)) = \triangle A''B''C''$.

The figure is rotated about the point where the two lines intersect, in
this case, point Q.

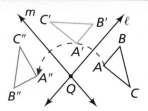

Problem 2 **Composing Reflections Across Intersecting Lines**

Got It? **a.** Use the diagram below. What is $(R_b \circ R_a)(J)$? What are the center and the angle of rotation for the resulting rotation?

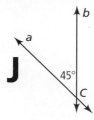

b. Reasoning Use the results of part (a) and Problem 2. Make a conjecture about the center of rotation and the angle of rotation for any rotation that is the result of any composition of reflections across two intersecting lines.

A Practice Find the image of each letter after the transformation $R_m \circ R_\ell$. What are the center and angle of rotation for the resulting rotation?

3.

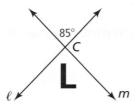

4.

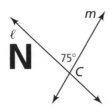

Any composition of isometries can be represented by a reflection, translation, rotation, or glide reflection. A **glide reflection** is the composition of a translation (a glide) and a reflection across a line parallel to the direction of translation. You can map a left paw print onto a right paw print with a glide reflection.

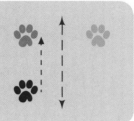

 Problem 3   Finding a Glide Reflection Image

Think

What is the direction of the translation?

Got It?   Graph $\triangle TEX$ from Problem 3. What is the image of $\triangle TEX$ for the glide reflection $(R_{y=-2} \circ T_{<1,\,0>})(\triangle TEX)$?

Practice   Graph $\triangle PNB$ and its image after the given transformation.

5. $(R_{y=0} \circ T_{<2,\,2>})(\triangle PNB)$

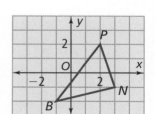

6. $(R_{y=x} \circ T_{<-1, 1>})(\triangle PNB)$

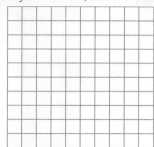

Lesson Check

Do you know HOW?

Sketch the image of Z reflected across line *a*, then across line *b*.

7.

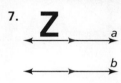

8.

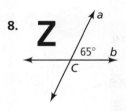

9. $\triangle PQR$ has vertices $P(0, 5)$, $Q(5, 3)$, and $R(3, 1)$. What are the vertices of the image of $\triangle PQR$ for the glide reflection $(R_{y=-2} \circ T_{<3, -1>})(\triangle PQR)$?

Do you UNDERSTAND?

© **10. Vocabulary** In a glide reflection, what is the relationship between the direction of the translation and the line of reflection?

© **11. Error Analysis** You reflect $\triangle DEF$ first across line m and then across line n. Your friend says you can get the same result by reflecting $\triangle DEF$ first across line n and then across line m. Explain your friend's error.

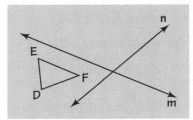

More Practice and Problem-Solving Exercises

B Apply

Use the given points and lines. Graph $\overline{AB}$ and its image $\overline{A''B''}$ after a reflection first across ℓ_1 and then across ℓ_2. Is the resulting transformation a translation or a rotation? For a translation, describe the direction and distance. For a rotation, tell the center of rotation and the angle of rotation.

12. $A(1, 5)$ and $B(2, 1)$; $\ell_1 : x = 3$; $\ell_2 : x = 7$

13. $A(2, 4)$ and $B(3, 1)$; $\ell_1 :$ x-axis; $\ell_2 :$ y-axis

14. $A(-4, -3)$ and $B(-4, 0)$; $\ell_1 : y = x$; $\ell_2 : y = -x$

15. $A(2, -5)$ and $B(-1, -3)$; $\ell_1 : y = 0$; $\ell_2 : y = 2$

16. $A(6, -4)$ and $B(5, 0)$; $\ell_1 : x = 6$; $\ell_2 : x = 4$

17. $A(-1, 0)$ and $B(0, -2)$; $\ell_1 : y = -1$; $\ell_2 : y = 1$

© **18. Think About a Plan** Let A' be the point $(1, 5)$. If $(R_{y=1} \circ T_{<3, 0>})(A) = A'$, then what are the coordinates of A?
   - How can you *work backwards* to find the coordinates of A?
   - Should A be to the left or to the right of A'?
   - Should A be above or below A'?

Describe the isometry that maps the blue figure onto the red figure.

19.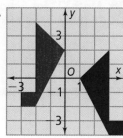

20.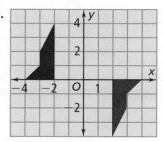

21. Which transformation maps the blue triangle onto the red triangle?

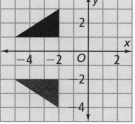

Ⓐ $R_{x=2} \circ T_{<0,-3>}$

Ⓑ $r_{(180°, O)}$

Ⓒ $R_{y=-\frac{1}{2}}$

Ⓓ $r_{(180°, O)} \circ R_{x\text{-axis}}$

Ⓖ **22. Writing** Reflections and glide reflections are *odd isometries*, while translations and rotations are *even isometries*. Use what you have learned in this lesson to explain why these categories make sense.

Ⓖ **23. Open-Ended** Draw △ABC. Describe a reflection, a translation, a rotation, and a glide reflection. Then draw the image of △ABC for each transformation.

Ⓖ **24. Reasoning** The definition states that a glide reflection is the composition of a translation and a reflection. Explain why these can occur in either order.

Identify each mapping as a translation, reflection, rotation, or glide reflection. Write the rule for each translation, reflection, rotation, or glide reflection. For glide reflections, write the rule as a composition of a translation and a reflection.

25. △ABC → △EDC

26. △EDC → △PQM

27. △MNJ → △EDC

28. △HIF → △HGF

29. △PQM → △JLM

30. △MNP → △EDC

31. △JLM → △MNJ

32. △PQM → △KJN

33. △KJN → △ABC

34. △HGF → △KJN

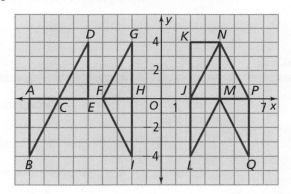

Ⓒ **Challenge**

35. Describe a glide reflection that maps the blue R to the red.

Ⓖ **36. Reasoning** Does an $x°$ rotation about a point P followed by a reflection across a line ℓ give the same image as a reflection across ℓ followed by an $x°$ rotation about P? Explain.

R

8-1 Translations

Quick Review

A **transformation** of a geometric figure is a change in its position, shape, or size.

A **translation** is a rigid motion that maps all points of a figure the same distance in the same direction.

In a **composition of transformations**, each transformation is performed on the image of the preceding transformation.

Example

What are the coordinates of $T_{<-2, 3>}(5, -9)$?

Add -2 to the x-coordinate, and 3 to the y-coordinate.

$(5, -9) \rightarrow (5 - 2, -9 + 3)$, or $(3, -6)$.

Exercises

1. a. A transformation maps *ZOWE* onto *LFMA*. Does the transformation appear to be a rigid motion? Explain.

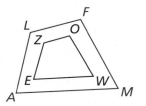

b. What is the image of $\overline{ZE}$? What is the preimage of *M*?

2. $\triangle RST$ has vertices $R(0, -4)$, $S(-2, -1)$, and $T(-6, 1)$. Graph $T_{<-4, 7>}(\triangle RST)$.

3. Write a rule to describe a translation 5 units left and 10 units up.

4. Find a single translation that has the same effect as the following composition of translations.

$T_{<-4, 7>}$ followed by $T_{<3, 0>}$

8-2 Reflections

Quick Review

The diagram shows a **reflection** across line r. A reflection is a rigid motion that preserves distance and angle measure. The image and preimage of a reflection have opposite orientations.

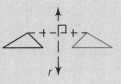

Example

Use points $P(1, 0)$, $Q(3, -2)$, and $R(4, 0)$. What is $R_{y\text{-axis}}(\triangle PQR)$?

Graph $\triangle PQR$. Find P', Q', and R' such that the y-axis is the perpendicular bisector of $\overline{PP'}$, $\overline{QQ'}$, and $\overline{RR'}$. Draw $\triangle P'Q'R'$.

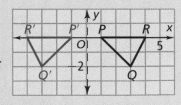

Exercises

Given points $A(6, 4)$, $B(-2, 1)$, and $C(5, 0)$, graph $\triangle ABC$ and each reflection image.

5. $R_{x\text{-axis}}(\triangle ABC)$ **6.** $R_{x = 4}(\triangle ABC)$

7. $R_{y = x}(\triangle ABC)$

8. Copy the diagram. Then draw $R_{y\text{-axis}}(BGHT)$. Label the vertices of the image by using prime notation.

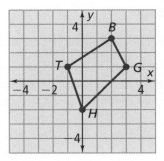

8-3 Rotations

Quick Review

The diagram shows a **rotation** of $x°$ about point R. A rotation is a rigid motion in which a figure and its image have the same orientation.

Example

$GHIJ$ has vertices $G(0, -3)$, $H(4, 1)$, $I(-1, 2)$, and $J(-5, -2)$. What are the vertices of $r_{(90°, O)}(GHIJ)$?

Use the rule $r_{(90°, O)}(x, y) = (-y, x)$.

$$r_{(90°, O)}(G) = (3, 0)$$
$$r_{(90°, O)}(H) = (-1, 4)$$
$$r_{(90°, O)}(I) = (-2, -1)$$
$$r_{(90°, O)}(J) = (2, -5)$$

Exercises

9. Copy the diagram below. Then draw $r_{(90°, P)}(\triangle ZXY)$. Label the vertices of the image by using prime notation.

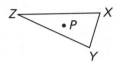

10. What are the coordinates of $r_{(180°, O)}(-4, 1)$?

11. $WXYZ$ is a quadrilateral with vertices $W(3, -1)$, $X(5, 2)$, $Y(0, 8)$, and $Z(2, -1)$. Graph $WXYZ$ and $r_{(270°, O)}(WXYZ)$.

8-4 Compositions of Isometries

Quick Review

An **isometry** is a transformation that preserves distance. All of the rigid motions, translations, reflections, and rotations, are isometries. A composition of isometries is also an isometry. All rigid motions can be expressed as a composition of reflections.

The diagram shows a **glide reflection** of N. A glide reflection is an isometry in which a figure and its image have opposite orientations.

Example

Describe the result of reflecting P first across line ℓ and then across line m.

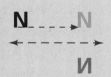

A composition of two reflections across intersecting lines is a rotation. The angle of rotation is twice the measure of the acute angle formed by the intersecting lines. P is rotated 100° about C.

Exercises

12. Sketch and describe the result of reflecting E first across line ℓ and then across line m.

Each figure is an isometry image of the figure at the right. Tell whether their orientations are the same or opposite. Then classify the isometry.

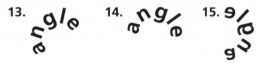

13. **14.** **15.**

16. $\triangle TAM$ has vertices $T(0, 5)$, $A(4, 1)$, and $M(3, 6)$. Find $R_{y = -2} \circ T_{<-4, 0>}(\triangle TAM)$.

Pull It All Together

Programming a Video Game

 ASSESSMENT

Alicia is a programmer for a company that makes video games. She is working on an interactive jigsaw puzzle. She needs to use transformations to write a program that will move the puzzle piece, shown by △*ABC*, into the target area, △*A′B′C′*.

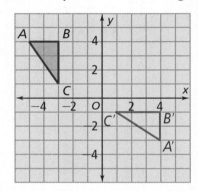

Alicia wants to write the program for two different cases, which correspond to two different levels of the game.

- Case 1: Reflections across any line are allowed.
- Case 2: Reflections across only the axes are allowed.

Alicia must convince her boss that the transformations she uses in each case move the puzzle piece to the target area in the minimum number of moves.

Task Description

Determine a composition of transformations that moves the puzzle piece to the target area for Case 1 and for Case 2. In each case, explain how you know that you have moved the piece in the minimum number of moves.

- What can you conclude by looking at the orientation of the puzzle piece and the orientation of the target area?
- How can you show that there is no single transformation that maps △*ABC* to △*A′B′C′*?

Get Ready!

Squaring Numbers

Simplify.

1. 6^2

2. 5^2

3. 12^2

Simplifying Expressions

Simplify each expression. Use 3.14 for π.

4. $3 \cdot 2.5 + 3 \cdot 1.5$

5. $\pi(2)^2$

6. $\sqrt{8^2 + 15^2}$

Evaluating Expressions

Evaluate the following expressions for $a = -3$ and $b = 7$.

7. $\frac{a+b}{2}$

8. $\frac{b-8}{4+a}$

9. $\sqrt{(2-a)^2 + (-5-b)^2}$

Finding Absolute Value

Simplify each absolute value expression.

10. $|-4|$

11. $|1 - 10|$

12. $|-6 - (-5)|$

Solving Equations

Algebra Solve each equation.

13. $8 = 3x - 7$

14. $4x - 5 = 7 - 2x$

15. $-1 - 3x = 5 - 3(2x + 4)$

 Looking Ahead Vocabulary

16. A building or a monument can have a *base* and a *height*. What are the *base* and the *height* of a parallelogram?

17. The *altitude* of an airplane is the height of the airplane above ground. What do you think an *altitude* of a parallelogram is?

CHAPTER 9

Connecting Algebra and Geometry

Big Ideas

1 Measurement
Essential Question How do you find the area and perimeter of a polygon?

2 Coordinate Geometry
Essential Question How can you use coordinate geometry to prove general relationships?

© Domains

- Expressing Geometric Properties with Equations
- Quantities

Chapter Preview

9-1 Perimeter and Area in the Coordinate Plane

9-2 Areas of Parallelograms and Triangles

9-3 Areas of Trapezoids, Rhombuses, and Kites

9-4 Polygons in the Coordinate Plane

Interactive Digital Path

Log in to **pearsonsuccessnet.com** and click on Interactive Digital Path to access the Solve Its and animated Problems.

🔊 Vocabulary

English/Spanish Vocabulary Audio Online:

English	Spanish
area, *p. 545*	segmentos congruentes
base of a parallelogram, *p. 559*	base de paralelogramo
base of a triangle, *p. 561*	base de un triangulo
height of a parallelogram, *p. 559*	alture de un paralelogramo
height of a trapezoid, *p. 568*	altura de un trapecio
height of a triangle, *p. 561*	altura de un triangulo
perimeter, *p. 545*	perímetro

Perimeter and Area in the Coordinate Plane

MCC9-12.G.GPE.7 Use coordinates to compute perimeters of polygons and areas of triangles and rectangles . . . Also **MCC9-12.N.Q.1**

Objectives To find the perimeter or circumference of basic shapes
To find the area of basic shapes

Solve It! Write your solution to the Solve It in the space below.

In the Solve It, you considered various ideas of what it means to take up space on a flat surface.

Essential Understanding Perimeter and area are two different ways of measuring geometric figures.

The **perimeter** P of a polygon is the sum of the lengths of its sides. The **area** A of a polygon is the number of square units it encloses. For figures such as squares, rectangles, triangles, and circles, you can use formulas for perimeter (or *circumference C* for circles) and area.

take note

Key Concept   Perimeter, Circumference, and Area

Square

side length s

$P = 4s$

$A = s^2$

s

Triangle

side lengths a, b, and c, base b, and height h

$P = a + b + c$

$A = \frac{1}{2}bh$

Rectangle

base b and height h

$P = 2b + 2h$, or

$\quad 2(b + h)$

$A = bh$

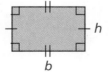

h

b

Circle

radius r and diameter d

$C = \pi d$, or $C = 2\pi r$

$A = \pi r^2$

The units of measurement for perimeter and circumference include inches, feet, yards, miles, centimeters, and meters. When measuring area, use square units such as square inches (in.^{2}), square feet (ft^2), square yards (yd^2), square miles (mi^2), square centimeters (cm^2), and square meters (m^2).

 **Problem 1** **Finding the Perimeter and Area of a Rectangle in the Coordinate Plane**

Got It? Rectangle *HIJK* has vertices $H(-5, -3)$, $I(-5, 2)$, $J(2, 2)$, and $K(2, -3)$. What is the perimeter of rectangle *HIJK*? What is the area of rectangle *HIJK*?

Ⓐ Practice **Find the perimeter and area of each rectangle.**

1. rectangle *ABCD* with vertices $A(2, 4)$, $B(2, 9)$, $C(5, 9)$, and $D(5, 4)$

2. rectangle *EFGH* with vertices $E(-3, 1)$, $F(-3, 6)$, $G(2, 6)$, and $H(2, 1)$

You can name a circle with the symbol ⊙. For example, the circle with center A is written ⊙A.

The formulas for a circle involve the special number *pi* (π). Pi is the ratio of any circle's circumference to its diameter. Since π is an irrational number,

$$\pi = 3.1415926\ldots,$$

you cannot write it as a terminating decimal. For an approximate answer, you can use 3.14 or $\frac{22}{7}$ for π. You can also use the ⓟ key on your calculator to get a rounded decimal for π. For an exact answer, leave the result in terms of π.

 **Problem 2** **Finding Circumference**

Plan

How do you decide which formula to use?

Got it?   **a.** What is the circumference of a circle with radius 24 m in terms of π?

b. What is the circumference of a circle with diameter 24 m to the nearest tenth?

 Practice   Find the circumference of ⊙C in terms of π.

3.

5 ft

C

4.

$\frac{1}{4}$ m

C

ONLINE PROBLEMS

Problem 3 **Finding Perimeter and Area of a Triangle in the Coordinate Plane**

Got It?   Triangle ABC has vertices $A(-6, 4)$, $B(6, 4)$, and $C(-6, -1)$. What is the perimeter of $\triangle ABC$? What is the area of $\triangle ABC$?

Ⓐ Practice Find the perimeter and area of each triangle.

5. triangle JKL with vertices $J(1, -1)$, $K(1, 5)$, and $L(9, -1)$

6. triangle *MNP* with vertices *M*(−5, −3), *N*(5, 2), and *P*(5, −3)

Problem 4 **Finding the Perimeter of a Pentagon in the Coordinate Plane**

Think

Do you need to calculate the length of each side?

Got It? Pentagon *JKLMN* has vertices *J*(−2, 5), *K*(1, 1), *L*(1, −4), *M*(−5, −4), and *N*(−5, 1). What is the perimeter of *JKLMN*?

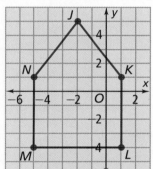

Practice In Exercises 7 and 8, find the perimeter of each pentagon.

7. pentagon *MNPQR* with vertices *M*(1, 6), *N*(5, 10), *P*(9, 6), *Q*(9, 1), and *R*(1, 1)

8. pentagon $RSTUV$ with vertices $R(-6, 2)$, $S(-3, 6)$, $T(5, 6)$, $U(5, -2)$, and $V(-3, -2)$

Problem 5   **Finding Area of a Circle**

Got It?   The diameter of a circle is 14 ft.

     a. What is the area of the circle in terms of π?

     b. What is the area of the circle using an approximation of π?

     ⓒ **c. Reasoning**   Which approximation of π did you use in part (b)? Why?

Practice Find the area of each circle in terms of π.

9.

20 m

10.

$\frac{3}{4}$ in.

The following postulate is useful in finding areas of figures with irregular shapes.

take note

Postulate 10 Area Addition Postulate

The area of a region is the sum of the areas of its nonoverlapping parts.

Problem 6 **Finding Area of an Irregular Shape**

Got It? **a. Reasoning** What is another way to separate the figure in Problem 6?

b. What is the area of the figure at the right?

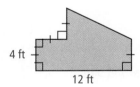

4 ft

12 ft

Ⓐ Practice Find the area of the shaded region. All angles are right angles.

11.

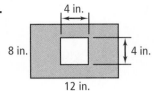

12.

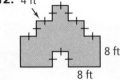

Lesson Check

Do you know HOW?

13. What is the perimeter and area of a rectangle with base 3 in. and height 7 in.?

14. What is the circumference and area of each circle to the nearest tenth?

    a. $r = 9$ in.
                                              b. $d = 7.3$ m

15. What is the perimeter and area of the figure at the right?

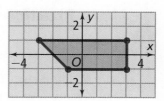

Do you UNDERSTAND?

16. Writing Describe a real-world situation in which you would need to find a perimeter. Then describe a situation in which you would need to find an area.

17. Compare and Contrast Your friend can't remember whether $2\pi r$ computes the circumference or the area of a circle. How would you help your friend? Explain.

18. Error Analysis A classmate finds the area of a circle with radius 30 in. to be 900 in.^{2}. What error did your classmate make?

More Practice and Problem-Solving Exercises

B Apply

Home Maintenance To determine how much of each item to buy, tell whether you need to know area or perimeter. Explain your choice.

19. wallpaper for a bedroom

20. crown molding for a ceiling

21. fencing for a backyard

22. paint for a basement floor

23. Think About a Plan A light-year unit describes the distance that one photon of light travels in one year. The Milky Way galaxy has a diameter of about 100,000 light-years. The distance to Earth from the center of the Milky Way galaxy is about 30,000 light-years. How many more light-years does a star on the outermost edge of the Milky Way travel in one full revolution around the galaxy compared to Earth?
   - What do you know about the shape of each orbital path?
   - Are you looking for circumference or area?
   - How do you compare the paths using algebraic expressions?

24. a. What is the area of a square with sides 12 in. long? 1 ft long?
   b. How many square inches are in a square foot?

25. a. Count squares to find the area of the entire figure at the right.
   b. Use a formula to find the area of each square outlined in red.
   c. Writing How does the sum of your results in part (b) compare to your result in part (a)? Which postulate does this support?

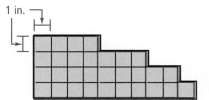

26. The area of an 11-cm-wide rectangle is 176 cm². What is its length?

27. Garden A scale drawing on a coordinate plane shows a rectangular garden. One unit represents one yard. The vertices of the garden are located at $(-12, -6)$, $(-12, -1)$, $(-2, -1)$, and $(-2, -6)$. What are the perimeter and area of the garden?

28. Tiling A scale drawing on a coordinate plane shows the plans for a rectangular kitchen. One unit represents one foot. The vertices of the kitchen are at $(-6, 7)$, $(2, 7)$, $(2, -5)$, and $(-6, -5)$. You want to tile the kitchen floor. Each tile is 2 feet by 2 feet. How many tiles will you need for the kitchen floor?

29. A square and a rectangle have equal areas. The rectangle is 64 cm by 81 cm. What is the perimeter of the square?

30. A rectangle has perimeter 40 cm and base 12 cm. What is its area?

Find the area of each shaded figure.

31. compact disc

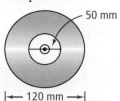

50 mm

|← 120 mm →|

32. drafting triangle

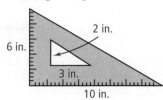

2 in.

6 in.

3 in.

10 in.

33. picture frame

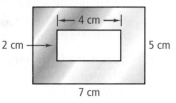

|← 4 cm →|

2 cm →

5 cm

7 cm

Ⓖ **34. Open-Ended** Draw a right triangle on a coordinate plane that has an area of 27 square units.

35. Baseball Sarah drew the outline of a pentagonal home plate on a coordinate plane where each unit represents one centimeter. The vertices of home plate are $(-22.5, 0)$, $(-22.5, 22)$, $(0, 44.5)$, $(22.5, 22)$, and $(22.5, 0)$. What is the perimeter of the home plate? Round to the nearest tenth.

Ⓖ **36. a. Reasoning** Can you use the formula for the perimeter of a rectangle to find the perimeter of any square? Explain.

  b. Can you use the formula for the perimeter of a square to find the perimeter of any rectangle? Explain.

  c. Use the formula for the perimeter of a square to write a formula for the area of a square in terms of its perimeter.

Ⓖ **37. Estimation** On an art trip to England, a student sketches the floor plan of the main body of Salisbury Cathedral. The shape of the floor plan is called the building's "footprint." The student estimates the dimensions of the cathedral on her sketch at the right. Use the student's lengths to estimate the area of Salisbury Cathedral's footprint.

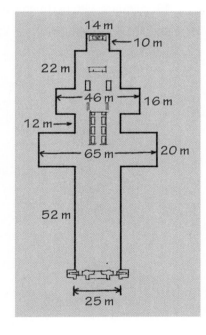

14 m

10 m

22 m

46 m

16 m

12 m →

65 m

20 m

52 m

25 m

38. Coordinate Geometry The endpoints of a diameter of a circle are $A(2, 1)$ and $B(5, 5)$. Find the area of the circle in terms of π.

39. Algebra A rectangle has a base of x units. The area is $(4x^2 - 2x)$ square units. What is the height of the rectangle in terms of x?

Ⓐ $(4 - x)$ units

Ⓒ $(x - 2)$ units

Ⓑ $(4x^3 - 2x^2)$ units

Ⓓ $(4x - 2)$ units

Coordinate Geometry Graph each rectangle in the coordinate plane. Find its perimeter and area.

40. $A(-3, 2)$, $B(-2, 2)$, $C(-2, -2)$, $D(-3, -2)$

41. $A(-2, -6)$, $B(-2, -3)$, $C(3, -3)$, $D(3, -6)$

42. You are drawing a right triangle on a coordinate plane. Two of the vertices are $(3, 0)$ and $(3, -4)$. Name a third point that you can plot so that the perimeter of the right triangle is 12 units.

43. You are drawing a pentagon on a coordinate plane. Four of the vertices are $(-1, 5)$, $(3, 5)$, $(3, -3)$, and $(-1, -3)$. Name a fifth point that can you can plot so that the perimeter of the pentagon is 26 units.

44. The surface area of a three-dimensional figure is the sum of the areas of all of its surfaces. You can find the surface area by finding the area of a net for the figure.

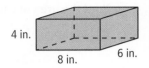

4 in. 8 in. 6 in.

    a. Draw a net for the solid shown. Label the dimensions.

    b. What is the area of the net? What is the surface area of the solid?

45. Coordinate Geometry On graph paper, draw polygon *ABCDEFG* with vertices $A(1, 1)$, $B(10, 1)$, $C(10, 8)$, $D(7, 5)$, $E(4, 5)$, $F(4, 8)$, and $G(1, 8)$. Find the perimeter and the area of the polygon.

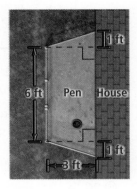

1 ft
6 ft Pen House
1 ft
3 ft

46. Pet Care You want to adopt a puppy from your local animal shelter. First, you plan to build an outdoor playpen along the side of your house, as shown on the right. You want to lay down special dog grass for the pen's floor. If dog grass costs $1.70 per square foot, how much will you spend?

47. A rectangular garden has an 8-ft walkway around it. How many more feet is the outer perimeter of the walkway than the perimeter of the garden?

Ⓒ Challenge

Algebra Find the area of each figure.

48. a rectangle with side lengths $\frac{2a}{5b}$ units and $\frac{3b}{8}$ units

49. a square with perimeter $10n$ units

50. a triangle with base $(5x - 2y)$ units and height $(4x + 3y)$ units

Partitioning a Segment

MCC9-12.G.GPE.6 Find the point on a directed line segment . . . that partitions the segment in a given ratio.

You have used the Midpoint Formula to find an endpoint of a segment. You can also use proportional reasoning to find points on a segment other than the endpoints.

Example

The endpoints of $\overline{LM}$ are $L(-4, 1)$ and $M(5, -5)$. Point N lies on $\overline{LM}$ and is $\frac{2}{3}$ of the way from L to M. What are the coordinates of point N?

Step 1 Plot $\overline{LM}$ on a coordinate plane.

Step 2 Notice that the segment drops 6 units vertically and runs 9 units horizontally as you go from L to M.

Divide the horizontal and vertical distances by 3 to break $\overline{LM}$ into thirds.

vertical distance: $\frac{6}{3} = 2$

horizontal distance: $\frac{9}{3} = 3$

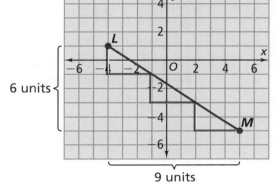

Step 3 Beginning at point L, drop 2 units down and move 3 units to the right to arrive at $(-1, -1)$. Repeat this process twice more to find the points $(2, -3)$ and $M(5, -5)$.

The points $(-1, -1)$ and $(2, -3)$ divide $\overline{LM}$ into thirds. The point $(2, -3)$ lies on $\overline{LM}$ and is $\frac{2}{3}$ of the way from L to M. The coordinates of point N are $(2, -3)$.

Exercises

1. The endpoints of $\overline{RS}$ are $R(-5, -2)$ and $S(3, 2)$. Point T lies on $\overline{RS}$ and is $\frac{1}{4}$ of the way from R to S. What are the coordinates of point T?

2. The endpoints of $\overline{CD}$ are $C(-6, -2)$ and $D(6, 4)$. Point E lies on $\overline{CD}$ and is $\frac{1}{3}$ of the way from C to D. What are the coordinates of point E?

3. Clarence is making a scale model of his neighborhood using a coordinate grid. He plots his school at point $S(4, 5)$ and the park at point $P(16, 11)$ along Elm Street as shown.

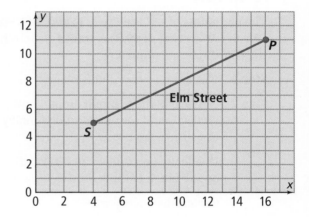

a. The bank is located on Elm Street and is $\frac{1}{6}$ of the way from the school to the park. What are the coordinates of the bank?

b. The grocery store is located on Elm Street and is $\frac{2}{3}$ of the way from the school to the park. What are the coordinates of the grocery store?

9-2 Areas of Parallelograms and Triangles

MCC9-12.G.GPE.7 Use coordinates to compute perimeters of polygons and areas of triangles and rectangles . . .
Also MCC9-12.G.MG.1

Objective To find the area of parallelograms and triangles

Solve It! Write your solution to the Solve It in the space below.

Essential Understanding You can find the area of a parallelogram or a triangle when you know the length of its base and its height.

A parallelogram with the same base and height as a rectangle has the same area as the rectangle.

take note

Key Concept Area of a Rectangle

The area of a rectangle is the product of its base and height.

$A = bh$

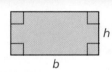

Key Concept Area of a Parallelogram

The area of a parallelogram is the product of a base and the corresponding height.

$A = bh$

A **base of a parallelogram** can be any one of its sides. The corresponding **altitude** is a segment perpendicular to the line containing that base, drawn from the side opposite the base. The **height** is the length of an altitude.

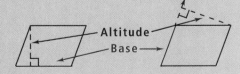

Got It?   What is the area of a parallelogram with base length 12 m and height 9 m?

Practice   Find the area of each parallelogram.

1.

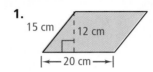

2.

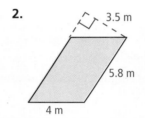

Got It?   A parallelogram has sides of length 15 cm and 18 cm. The height corresponding to a 15-cm base is 9 cm. What is the height corresponding to an 18-cm base?

> **Think**
> How can a diagram help you visualize the problem?

Practice Find the value of *h* for each parallelogram.

3.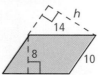

4.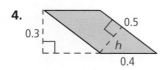

 You can rotate a triangle about the midpoint of a side to form a parallelogram.

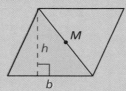

The area of the triangle is half the area of the parallelogram.

take note

Key Concept   Area of a Triangle

The area of a triangle is half the product of a base and the corresponding height.

$A = \frac{1}{2}bh$

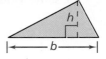

A **base of a triangle** can be any of its sides. The corresponding **height** is the length of the altitude to the line containing that base.

Problem 3 **Finding the Area of a Triangle**

Got It? What is the area of the triangle?

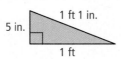

Think

In what units should your final answer be written?

A **Practice** Find the area of each triangle.

5.

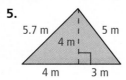

6.

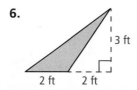

Problem 4 **Finding the Area of an Irregular Figure**

Got It? **Reasoning** Suppose the base lengths of the square and triangle in Problem 4 are doubled to 12 in., but the height of each polygon remains the same. How is the area of the figure affected?

Practice   7. **Urban Design** A bakery has a
50 ft-by-31 ft parking lot. The four
parking spaces are parallelograms
with the same dimensions, the
driving region is a rectangle,
and the two areas for flowers
are triangles with the same
dimensions.

   a. Find the area of the paved
      surface by adding the areas of
      the driving region and the four
      parking spaces.

   b. Describe another method for finding the area of the paved surface.

   c. Use your method from part (b) to find the area. Then compare
      answers from parts (a) and (b) to check your work.

Lesson Check

Do you know HOW?

Find the area of each parallelogram.

8.
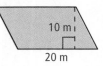
10 m
20 m

9.

8 ft
8 ft

Find the area of each triangle.

10.

12 cm
16 cm

11.

8 in.
9 in.

Do you UNDERSTAND?

MATHEMATICAL
PRACTICES

12. **Vocabulary** Does an altitude of a triangle have to lie inside the triangle? Explain.

13. **Writing** How can you show that a parallelogram and a rectangle with the same bases and heights have equal areas?

14. $\square ABCD$ is divided into two triangles along diagonal $\overline{AC}$. If you know the area of the parallelogram, how do you find the area of $\triangle ABC$?

More Practice and Problem-Solving Exercises

B Apply

15. The area of a parallelogram is 24 in.² and the height is 6 in. Find the length of the corresponding base.

16. What is the area of the figure shown at the right?

    (A) 64 cm²   (C) 96 cm²

    (B) 88 cm²   (D) 112 cm²

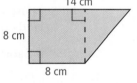

17. A right isosceles triangle has area 98 cm². Find the length of each leg.

18. **Algebra** The area of a triangle is 108 in.². A base and corresponding height are in the ratio 3 : 2. Find the length of the base and the corresponding height.

19. **Think About a Plan** Ki used geometry software to create the figure shown at the right. She constructed $\overleftrightarrow{AB}$ and a point C not on $\overleftrightarrow{AB}$. Then she constructed line k parallel to $\overleftrightarrow{AB}$ through point C. Next, Ki constructed point D on line k as well as $\overline{AD}$ and $\overline{BD}$. She dragged point D along line k to manipulate $\triangle ABD$. How does the area of $\triangle ABD$ change? Explain.

    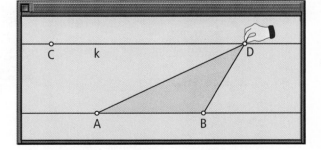

    - Which dimensions of the triangle change when Ki drags point D?
    - Do the lengths of $\overline{AD}$ and $\overline{BD}$ matter when calculating area?

@ **20. Open-Ended** Using graph paper, draw an acute triangle, an obtuse triangle, and a right triangle, each with area 12 units².

Find the area of each figure.

21. □*ABJF*

22. △*BDJ*

23. △*DKJ*

24. □*BDKJ*

25. □*ADKF*

26. △*BCJ*

27. trapezoid *ADJF*

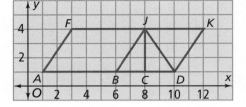

@ **28. Reasoning** Suppose the height of a triangle is tripled. How does this affect the area of the triangle? Explain.

For Exercises 29–32, (a) graph the lines and (b) find the area of the triangle enclosed by the lines.

29. $y = x$, $x = 0$, $y = 7$

30. $y = x + 2$, $y = 2$, $x = 6$

31. $y = -\frac{1}{2}x + 3$, $y = 0$, $x = -2$

32. $y = \frac{3}{4}x - 2$, $y = -2$, $x = 4$

@ **33. Probability** Your friend drew these three figures on a grid. A fly lands at random at a point on the grid.

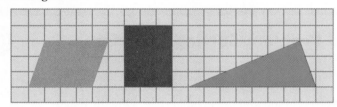

   a. Writing Is the fly more likely to land on one of the figures or on the blank grid? Explain.

   b. Suppose you know the fly lands on one of the figures. Is the fly more likely to land on one figure than on another? Explain.

Coordinate Geometry Find the area of a polygon with the given vertices.

34. $A(3, 9)$, $B(8, 9)$, $C(2, -3)$, $D(-3, -3)$

35. $E(1, 1)$, $F(4, 5)$, $G(11, 5)$, $H(8, 1)$

36. $D(0, 0)$, $E(2, 4)$, $F(6, 4)$, $G(6, 0)$

37. $K(-7, -2)$, $L(-7, 6)$, $M(1, 6)$, $N(7, -2)$

Find the area of each figure.

38.

39.

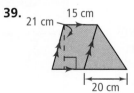

40.

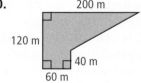

 **Challenge**

History The Greek mathematician Heron is most famous for this formula for the area of a triangle in terms of the lengths of its sides *a*, *b*, and *c*.

$$A = \sqrt{s(s - a)(s - b)(s - c)}, \text{ where } s = \tfrac{1}{2}(a + b + c)$$

Use Heron's Formula and a calculator to find the area of each triangle. Round your answer to the nearest whole number.

41. *a* = 8 in., *b* = 9 in., *c* = 10 in.

42. *a* = 15 m, *b* = 17 m, *c* = 21 m

43. **a.** Use Heron's Formula to find the area of this triangle.
    b. Verify your answer to part (a) by using the formula $A = \tfrac{1}{2}bh$.

15 in.

9 in.

12 in.

Areas of Trapezoids, Rhombuses, and Kites

MCC9-12.G.MG.1 Use geometric shapes, their measures, and their properties to describe objects . . . Also
Extends **MCC9-12.G.GPE.7**

Objective To find the area of a trapezoid, rhombus, or kite

Solve It! Write your solution to the Solve It in the space below.

Essential Understanding You can find the area of a trapezoid when you
know its height and the lengths of its bases.

The **height of a trapezoid** is the perpendicular distance between the bases.

Key Concept   Area of a Trapezoid

The area of a trapezoid is half the product of the height
and the sum of the bases.

$$A = \tfrac{1}{2}h(b_1 + b_2)$$

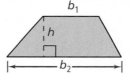

Problem 1   Area of a Trapezoid

Got It? What is the area of a trapezoid with height 7 cm and bases 12 cm
and 15 cm?

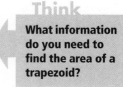

Think

**What information
do you need to
find the area of a
trapezoid?**

Find the area of each trapezoid.

1.

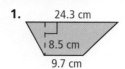

24.3 cm

8.5 cm

9.7 cm

2.

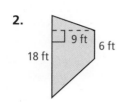

9 ft

6 ft

18 ft

Essential Understanding You can find the area of a rhombus or a kite when you know the lengths of its diagonals.

take note

Key Concept   Area of a Rhombus or a Kite

The area of a rhombus or a kite is half the product of the lengths of its diagonals.

$A = \frac{1}{2}d_1 d_2$

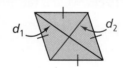

d_1 d_2

Rhombus

d_1

d_2

Kite

Problem 2   **Finding the Area of a Kite**

Got It?   What is the area of a kite with diagonals that are 12 in. and 9 in. long?

A **Practice** Find the area of each kite.

3.

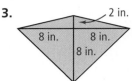

2 in.

8 in.   8 in.

8 in.

4.

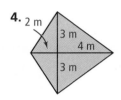

2 m

3 m

4 m

3 m

 Problem 3 **Finding the Area of a Rhombus**

Got It? A rhombus has sides 10 cm long. If the length of the longer diagonal is 16 cm, what is the area of the rhombus?

Think

How can drawing a diagram help you visualize the problem?

A **Practice** Find the area of each rhombus.

5.

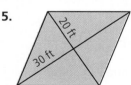

20 ft

30 ft

6.

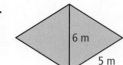

Lesson Check

Do you know HOW?

Find the area of each figure.

7.

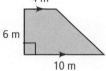

4 m

6 m

10 m

8.

15 in.

18 in.

27 in.

9.

3 ft

5 ft

10.

12 in.

12 in.

11.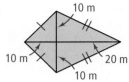

12.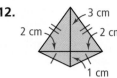

Do you UNDERSTAND?

MATHEMATICAL
PRACTICES

13. Vocabulary Can a trapezoid and a parallelogram with the same base and height have the same area? Explain.

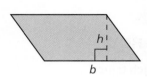

14. Reasoning Do you need to know all the side lengths to find the area of a trapezoid?

15. Reasoning Can you find the area of a rhombus if you only know the lengths of its sides? Explain.

16. Reasoning Do you need to know the lengths of the sides to find the area of a kite? Explain.

More Practice and Problem-Solving Exercises

B Apply

17. Think About a Plan A trapezoid has two right angles, 12-m and 18-m bases, and an 8-m height. Sketch the trapezoid and find its perimeter and area.
  • Are the right angles consecutive or opposite angles?
  • How does knowing the height help you find the perimeter?

18. Metallurgy The end of a gold bar has the shape of a trapezoid with the measurements shown. Find the area of the end.

19. Open-Ended Draw a kite. Find the lengths of its diagonals. Find its area.

Find the area of each trapezoid to the nearest tenth.

20.

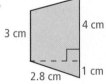

3 cm
4 cm
2.8 cm
1 cm

21.

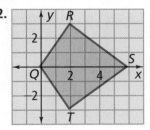

2.1 m
0.9 m
1.2 m

Coordinate Geometry Find the area of quadrilateral *QRST*.

22.

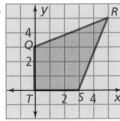

23.

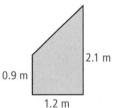

24.

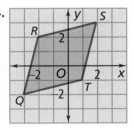

25. a. Coordinate Geometry Graph the lines $x = 0$, $x = 6$, $y = 0$, and $y = x + 4$.
  b. What type of quadrilateral do the lines form?
  c. Find the area of the quadrilateral.

26. **Visualization** The kite has diagonals d_1 and d_2 congruent to the sides of the rectangle. Explain why the area of the kite is $\frac{1}{2}d_1d_2$.

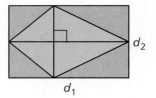

27. Draw a trapezoid. Label its bases b_1 and b_2 and its height h. Then draw a diagonal of the trapezoid.
    a. Write equations for the area of each of the two triangles formed.
    b. **Writing** Explain how you can justify the trapezoid area formula using the areas of the two triangles.

Challenge

28. **Algebra** One base of a trapezoid is twice the other. The height is the average of the two bases. The area is 324 cm². Find the height and the bases. (*Hint:* Let the smaller base be x.)

29. **Sports** Ty wants to paint one side of the skateboarding ramp he built. The ramp is 4 m wide. Its surface is modeled by the equation $y = 0.25x^2$. Use the trapezoids and triangles shown to estimate the area to be painted.

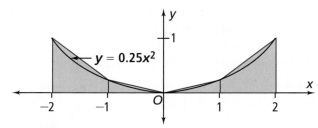

Proving Slope Criteria for Parallel and Perpendicular Lines

MCC9-12.G.GPE.5 Prove the slope criteria for parallel and perpendicular lines and use them to solve geometric problems . . .

You can determine whether two nonvertical lines on a coordinate plane are parallel by examining their slopes.

Activity 1

Let two nonvertical parallel lines in the coordinate plane be given in slope-intercept form by the equations $y = m_1x + b_1$ and $y = m_2x + b_2$.

1. How are b_1 and b_2 related? Can $b_2 - b_1$ be equal to 0? Explain.

2. How many solutions does the equation $m_1x + b_1 = m_2x + b_2$ have? Explain.

3. Show that the equation in Exercise 2 is equivalent to $(m_1 - m_2)x = b_2 - b_1$.

4. When are there no solutions to the equation in Exercise 3? Explain.

5. Explain how your answer to Exercise 4 shows that if nonvertical lines are parallel, then their slopes are equal.

6. Show that if two distinct lines have the same slope, then they are parallel by showing that the equation $mx + b_1 = mx + b_2$ has no solutions when $b_1 \neq b_2$.

You can also determine whether two nonvertical lines on a coordinate plane are perpendicular by examining their slopes.

Activity 2

Let two perpendicular lines, neither of which is vertical, be given in slope-intercept form by the equations $y = m_1x + b_1$ and $y = m_2x + b_2$. Let the point of intersection be point A. Draw a horizontal segment $\overline{AP}$ with length 1. Draw a vertical line through point P that intersects the two perpendicular lines at points B and C. This is shown in the figure at the right.

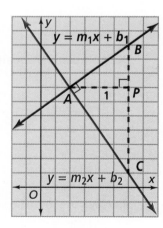

7. Use the slopes of the perpendicular lines to find the lengths of $\overline{BP}$ and $\overline{CP}$.

8. Use your results from Exercise 7 to find the lengths of $\overline{AB}$ and $\overline{AC}$.

9. Let the coordinates of A be (p, q). Show that the y-coordinates of B and C are $q + m_1$ and $q + m_2$, respectively.

10. Use your results from Exercise 9 to find the length of $\overline{BC}$.

11. Use the Pythagorean theorem to show that $m_1 m_2 = -1$.

Exercises

Determine whether the lines are *parallel, perpendicular,* or *neither*.

12. $y = 3x + 1$

$\qquad y = -\frac{1}{3}x - 1$

13. $y = \frac{1}{2}x + \frac{3}{2}$

$\qquad y = \frac{1}{2}x - \frac{2}{3}$

14. $y = \frac{2}{3}x - 4$

$\qquad y = \frac{3}{2}x - 4$

15. $y - 2 = 2(x + 1)$

$\qquad 4x - 2y = -8$

© **16. Reasoning** Can you use slope criteria for determining whether lines are parallel or perpendicular if one of the lines is vertical? Explain.

Polygons in the Coordinate Plane

MCC9-12.G.GPE.4 . . . Prove simple geometric theorems algebraically.

Objective   To classify polygons in the coordinate plane

Solve It!   Write your solution to the Solve It in the space below.

In the Solve It, you formed a polygon on a grid. In this lesson, you will classify polygons in the coordinate plane.

Essential Understanding   You can classify figures in the coordinate plane using the formulas for slope, distance, and midpoint.

The chart below reviews these formulas and tells when to use them.

take note

Key Concept   Formulas and the Coordinate Plane

Formula	When to Use It
Distance Formula $$d = \sqrt{(x_2 - x_1)^2 + (y_2 - y_1)^2}$$	To determine whether • sides are congruent • diagonals are congruent
Midpoint Formula $$M = \left(\frac{x_1 + x_2}{2}, \frac{y_1 + y_2}{2} \right)$$	To determine • the coordinates of the midpoint of a side • whether diagonals bisect each other
Slope Formula $$m = \frac{y_2 - y_1}{x_2 - x_1}$$	To determine whether • opposite sides are parallel • diagonals are perpendicular • sides are perpendicular

 **Problem 1** **Classifying a Triangle**

Got It? △*DEF* has vertices *D*(0, 0), *E*(1, 4), and *F*(5, 2). Show that △*DEF* is scalene.

Think

What formula should you use?

Ⓐ Practice Determine whether △*ABC* is *scalene, isosceles,* or *equilateral.* Explain.

1.

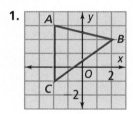

2.

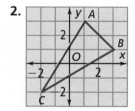

 **Problem 2** Classifying a Quadrilateral

Got It? Parallelogram *MNPQ* has vertices *M*(0, 1), *N*(−1, 4), *P*(2, 5), and *Q*(3, 2). Show that ▱*MNPQ* is a rectangle.

Think

How can you use slope to get information about the sides of a figure?

 **Practice** Show that the parallelogram with the given vertices is a rhombus.

3. *L*(1, 2), *M*(3, 3), *N*(5, 2), *P*(3, 1)

4. *S*(1, 3), *P*(4, 4), *A*(3, 1), *T*(0, 0)

Problem 3 Classifying a Quadrilateral

Got It? An isosceles trapezoid has vertices *A*(0, 0), *B*(2, 4), *C*(6, 4), and *D*(8, 0). Show that the quadrilateral formed by connecting the midpoints of the sides of *ABCD* is a rhombus.

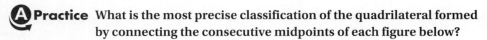

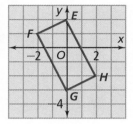

A Practice What is the most precise classification of the quadrilateral formed by connecting the consecutive midpoints of each figure below?

5. rectangle *EFGH*

6. isosceles trapezoid *JKLM*

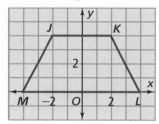

Lesson Check

Do you know HOW?

7. $\triangle TRI$ has vertices $T(-3, 4)$, $R(3, 4)$, and $I(0, 0)$. Is $\triangle TRI$ *scalene*, *isosceles*, or *equilateral*?

8. Is $QRST$ at the right a rectangle? Explain.

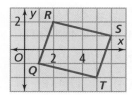

Do you UNDERSTAND?

MATHEMATICAL PRACTICES

9. Writing In the figure at the right, the blue points bisect the sides of the triangle. Describe how you would determine whether the lengths of the blue segments are equal.

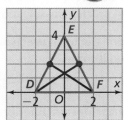

10. Error Analysis A student says that the quadrilateral with vertices $D(1, 2)$, $E(2, 0)$, $F(5, 4)$, and $G(6, 2)$ is a square because it has four right angles. What is the student's error?

More Practice and Problem-Solving Exercises

B Apply

Graph and label each triangle with the given vertices. Determine whether each triangle is *scalene, isosceles*, or *equilateral*. Then tell whether each triangle is a right triangle.

11. $T(1, 1)$, $R(3, 8)$, $I(6, 4)$

12. $J(-5, 0)$, $K(5, 8)$, $L(4, -1)$

13. $A(3, 2)$, $B(-10, 4)$, $C(-5, -8)$

14. $H(1, -2)$, $B(-1, 4)$, $F(5, 6)$

Graph and label each quadrilateral with the given vertices. Then determine the most precise name for each quadrilateral.

15. $P(-5, 0)$, $Q(-3, 2)$, $R(3, 2)$, $S(5, 0)$

16. $S(0, 0)$, $T(4, 0)$, $U(3, 2)$, $V(-1, 2)$

17. $F(0, 0)$, $G(5, 5)$, $H(8, 4)$, $I(7, 1)$

18. $M(-14, 4)$, $N(1, 6)$, $P(3, -9)$, $Q(-12, -11)$

19. $A(3, 5)$, $B(7, 6)$, $C(6, 2)$, $D(2, 1)$

20. $N(-6, 4)$, $P(-3, 1)$, $Q(0, 2)$, $R(-3, 5)$

21. $J(2, 1)$, $K(5, 4)$, $L(8, 1)$, $M(2, -3)$

22. $H(-2, -3)$, $I(4, 0)$, $J(3, 2)$, $K(-3, -1)$

23. $W(-1, 1)$, $X(0, 2)$, $Y(1, 1)$, $Z(0, -2)$

24. $D(-3, 1)$, $E(-7, -3)$, $F(6, -3)$, $G(2, 1)$

© 25. Think About a Plan Do the triangles at the right have the same side lengths? How do you know?
- Which formula should you use?
- What are the corresponding sides?

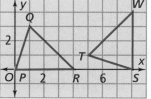

© 26. Reasoning A quadrilateral has opposite sides with equal slopes and consecutive sides with slopes that are negative reciprocals. What is the most precise classification of the quadrilateral? Explain.

Determine the most precise name for the quadrilateral with the given vertices. Then find its area.

27. $A(0, 2)$, $B(4, 2)$, $C(-3, -4)$, $D(-7, -4)$

28. $J(1, -3)$, $K(3, 1)$, $L(7, -1)$, $M(5, -5)$

29. Interior Design Interior designers often use grids to plan the placement of furniture in a room. The design at the right shows four chairs around a coffee table. The designer plans for cutouts of chairs on lattice points, where the grid lines intersect. She wants the chairs oriented at the vertices of a parallelogram. Does she need to fix her plan? If so, describe the change(s) she should make.

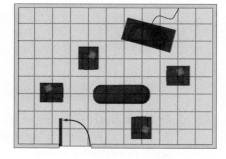

30. Use the diagram at the right.

    a. What is the most precise classification of *ABCD*?

    b. What is the most precise classification of *EFGH*?

    c. Do *ABCD* and *EFGH* have the same side lengths and angle measures? Explain.

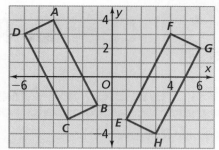

ⓒ Challenge

31. Coordinate Geometry The diagonals of quadrilateral *EFGH* intersect at *D*(−1, 4). *EFGH* has vertices at *E*(2, 7) and *F*(−3, 5). What must be the coordinates of *G* and *H* to ensure that *EFGH* is a parallelogram?

The endpoints of $\overline{AB}$ are *A*(−3, 5) and *B*(9, 15). Find the coordinates of the points that divide $\overline{AB}$ into the given number of congruent segments.

32. 4   **33.** 6   **34.** 10   **35.** 50   **36.** *n*

9-1 Perimeter and Area in the Coordinate Plane

Quick Review

The perimeter P of a polygon is the sum of the lengths of its sides. Circles have a circumference C. The area A of a polygon or a circle is the number of square units it encloses.

Square: $P = 4s$; $A = s^2$

Rectangle: $P = 2b + 2h$; $A = bh$

Triangle: $P = a + b + c$; $A = \frac{1}{2}bh$

Circle: $C = \pi d$ or $C = 2\pi r$; $A = \pi r^2$

Example

Find the perimeter and area of a rectangle with $b = 12$ m and $h = 8$ m.

$$P = 2b + 2h \qquad\qquad A = bh$$
$$= 2(12) + 2(8) \qquad = 12 \cdot 8$$
$$= 40 \qquad\qquad\quad = 96$$

The perimeter is 40 m and the area is 96 m².

Exercises

Find the perimeter and area of each figure.

1.

8 cm

2.

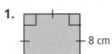

3 in.

5 in.

Find the circumference and the area for each circle in terms of π.

3. $r = 3$ in.

4. $d = 15$ m

9-2 Areas of Parallelograms and Triangles

Quick Review

You can find the area of a rectangle, a parallelogram, or a triangle if you know the **base** b and the **height** h.

The area of a rectangle or parallelogram is $A = bh$.

The area of a triangle is $A = \frac{1}{2}bh$.

Example

What is area of the parallelogram?

$A = bh$ Use the area formula.

$= (12)(8) = 96$ Substitute and simplify.

12 cm

8 cm

The area of the parallelogram is 96 cm².

Exercises

Find the area of each figure.

5.

5 m

4 m

6.

10 in.

9 in.

7.

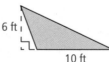

6 ft

10 ft

8.

10 ft

16 ft

9. A right triangle has legs measuring 5 ft and 12 ft, and hypotenuse measuring 13 ft. What is its area?

9-3 Areas of Trapezoids, Rhombuses, and Kites

Quick Review

The **height of a trapezoid** h is the perpendicular distance between the bases, b_1 and b_2.

The area of a trapezoid is $A = \frac{1}{2}h(b_1 + b_2)$.

The area of a rhombus or a kite is $A = \frac{1}{2}d_1 d_2$, where d_1 and d_2 are the lengths of its diagonals.

Example

What is the area of the trapezoid?

$$A = \tfrac{1}{2}h(b_1 + b_2) \quad \text{Use the area formula.}$$
$$= \tfrac{1}{2}(8)(7 + 3) \quad \text{Substitute.}$$
$$= 40 \quad \text{Simplify.}$$

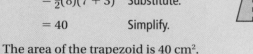

The area of the trapezoid is 40 cm².

Exercises

Find the area of each figure. If necessary, leave your answer in simplest radical form.

10.

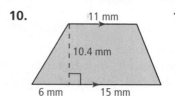

11.

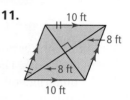

12.

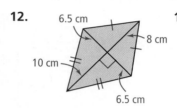

13.

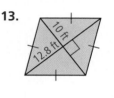

14. A trapezoid has a height of 6 m. The length of one base is three times the length of the other base. The sum of the base lengths is 18 m. What is the area of the trapezoid?

9-4 Polygons in the Coordinate Plane

Quick Review

To determine whether sides or diagonals are congruent, use the Distance Formula. To determine the coordinates of the midpoint of a side, or whether the diagonals bisect each other, use the Midpoint Formula. To determine whether opposite sides are parallel, or whether diagonals or sides are perpendicular, use the Slope Formula.

Example

$\triangle XYZ$ has vertices $X(1, 0)$, $Y(-2, -4)$, and $Z(4, -4)$. Is $\triangle XYZ$ *scalene*, *isosceles*, or *equilateral*?

To find the lengths of the legs, use the Distance Formula.

$$XY = \sqrt{(-2-1)^2 + (-4-0)^2} = \sqrt{9+16} = 5$$
$$YZ = \sqrt{(4-(-2))^2 + (-4-(-4))^2} = \sqrt{36+0} = 6$$
$$XZ = \sqrt{(4-1)^2 + (-4-0)^2} = \sqrt{9+16} = 5$$

Two side lengths are equal, so $\triangle XYZ$ is isosceles.

Exercises

Determine whether $\triangle ABC$ is *scalene*, *isosceles*, or *equilateral*.

15.

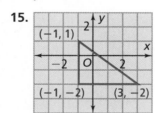

16.

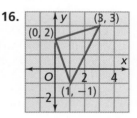

What is the most precise classification of the quadrilateral with the given vertices?

17. $G(2, 5)$, $R(5, 8)$, $A(-2, 12)$, $D(-5, 9)$

18. $F(-13, 7)$, $I(1, 12)$, $N(15, 7)$, $E(1, -5)$

19. $Q(4, 5)$, $U(12, 14)$, $A(20, 5)$, $D(12, -4)$

20. $W(-11, 4)$, $H(-9, 10)$, $A(2, 10)$, $T(4, 4)$

Pull It **All Together**

 ASSESSMENT

Finding the Area of a Plot of Land

A traveling carnival requires a plot of land with an area of at least 45 m² to set up one of their rides. The carnival's manager wants to know if the plot of land determined by quadrilateral *ABCD* on the coordinate plane below will work. Each unit of the coordinate plane represents one meter.

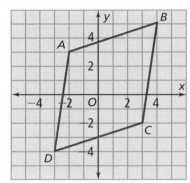

Task Description

Decide whether the plot of land determined by quadrilateral *ABCD* meets the carnival's requirements.

- How can you determine the type of quadrilateral formed by vertices *A*, *B*, *C*, and *D*?

- What lengths do you need to know in order to calculate the area of the quadrilateral?

Postulates

Postulate 1
Through any two points there is exactly one line.

Postulate 2
If two distinct lines intersect, then they intersect in exactly one point.

Postulate 3
If two distinct planes intersect, then they intersect in exactly one line.

Postulate 4
Through any three noncollinear points there is exactly on plane.

Postulate 5
Ruler Postulate
Every point on a line can be paired with a real number. This makes a one-to-one correspondence between the points on the line and the real numbers.

Postulate 6
Segment Addition Postulate
If three points A, B, and C are collinear and B is between A and C, then $AB + BC = AC$.

Postulate 7
Protractor Postulate
Consider $\overrightarrow{OB}$ and a point A on one side of $\overrightarrow{OB}$. Every ray of the form $\overrightarrow{OA}$ can be paired one to one with a real number from 0 to 180.

Postulate 8
Angle Addition Postulate
If point B is in the interior of $\angle AOC$, then $m\angle AOB + m\angle BOC = m\angle AOC$.

Postulate 9
Linear Pair Postulate
If two angles form a linear pair, then they are supplementary.

Postulate 10
Area Addition Postulate
The area of a region is the sum of the area of its nonoverlapping parts.

Visual **Glossary**

English	A	Spanish

Absolute value function (p. 219)   A function with a V-shaped graph that opens up or down. The parent function for the family of absolute value functions is $y = |x|$.

Función de valor absoluto (p. 219)   Función cuya gráfica forma una V que se abre hacia arriba o hacia abajo. La función madre de la familia de funciones de valor absoluto es $y = |x|$.

Example

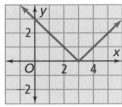

Accuracy (p. 49)   Accuracy is the degree of how close a measurement is to the true value of the measurement.

Exactitud (p. 49)   La exactitud es el grado de lo cerca que una medición está del valor verdadero de la cantidad que se mide.

Acute Angle (p. 460)   An acute angle is an angle whose measure is between 0 and 90.

Ángulo agudo (p. 460)   Un ángulo agudo es un ángulo que mide entre 0 y 90 grados.

Example

17°

Adjacent angles (p. 466)   Adjacent angles are two coplanar angles that have a common side and a common vertex but no common interior points.

Ángulos adyacentes (p. 466)   Los ángulos adyacentes son dos ángulos coplanarios que tienen un lado común y el mismo vértice, pero no tienen puntos interiores comunes.

Example

∠1 and ∠2 are adjacent.

∠3 and ∠4 are *not* adjacent.

Altitude (p. 559)   *See* parallelogram; trapezoid.

Altura (p. 559)   *Ver* parallelogram; trapezoid.

Angle (p. 458)   An angle is formed by two rays with the same endpoint. The rays are the *sides* of the angle and the common endpoint is the *vertex* of the angle.

Ángulo (p. 458)   Un ángulo está formado por dos semirrectas que convergen en un mismo extremo. Las semirrectas son los *lados* del ángulo y los extremos en común son el *vértice*.

Example

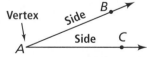

This angle could be named ∠A, ∠BAC, or ∠CAB.

English

Spanish

Angle bisector (p. 471) An angle bisector is a ray that divides an angle into two congruent angles.

Bisectriz de un ángulo (p. 471) La bisectriz de un ángulo es una semirrecta que divide al ángulo en dos ángulos congruentes.

Example

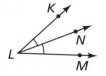

$\overrightarrow{LN}$ bisects $\angle KLM$.

$\angle KLN \cong \angle NLM$.

Angle of rotation (p. 515) *See* rotation.

Ángulo de rotación (p. 515) *Ver* rotation.

Area (p. 545) The area of a plane figure is the number of square units enclosed by the figure.

Área (p. 545) El área de una figura plana es la cantidad de unidades cuadradas que contiene la figura.

Example

The area of the rectangle is 12 square units, or 12 units^2.

Arithmetic sequence (p. 148) A number sequence formed by adding a fixed number to each previous term to find the next term. The fixed number is called the common difference.

Progresión aritmética (p. 148) En una progresión aritmética la diferencia entre términos consecutivos es un número constante. El número constante se llama la diferencia común.

Example 4, 7, 10, 13, . . . is an arithmetic sequence.

Average rate of change (p. 303) The average rate of change of a function over the interval $a \leq x \leq b$ is equal to $\frac{f(b) - f(a)}{b - a}$.

Tasa media de cambio (p. 303) La tasa media de cambio de una función sobre el intervalo $a \leq x \leq b$ es igual a $\frac{f(b) - f(a)}{b - a}$.

Example The average rate of change of the function $f(x) = x^2 - 2x + 2$ over the interval

$1 \leq x \leq 4$ is $\frac{f(4) - f(1)}{4 - 1} = \frac{9}{3} = 3$

Axiom (p. 444) *See* postulate.

Axioma (p. 444) *Ver* postulate.

B

Box-and-whisker plot (p. 394) A graph that summarizes data along a number line. The left whisker extends from the minimum to the first quartile. The box extends from the first quartile to the third quartile and has a vertical line through the median. The right whisker extends from the third quartile to the maximum.

Gráfica de cajas (p. 394) Gráfica que resume los datos a lo largo de una recta numérica. El brazo izquierdo se extiende desde el valor mínimo del primer cuartil. La caja se extiende desde el primer cuartil hasta el tercer cuartil y tiene una línea vertical que atraviesa la mediana. El brazo derecho se extiende desde el tercer cuartil hasta el valor máximo.

Example

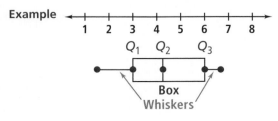

Causation (p. 405)   When a change in one quantity causes a change in a second quantity. A correlation between quantities does not always imply causation.

Causalidad (p. 405)   Cuando un cambio en una cantidad causa un cambio en una segunda cantidad. Una correlación entre las cantidades no implica siempre la causalidad.

Center (p. 515)   *See* rotation.

Centro (p. 515)   *Ver* rotation.

Circle (p. 460)   A circle is the set of all points in a plane that are given distance, the *radius*, from a given point, the *center*.

Círculo (p. 460)   Un círculo es el conjunto de todos los puntos de un plano situados a una distancia dada, el *radio*, e un punto dado, el *centro*.

Coefficient (p. 6)   The numerical factor when a term has a variable.

Coeficiente (p. 6)   Factor numérico de un término que contiene una variable.

Example   In the expression $2x + 3y + 16$, 2 and 3 are coefficients.

Collinear points (p. 442)   Collinear points lie on the same line.

Puntos colineales (p. 442)   Los puntos colineales son los que están sobre la misma recta.

Example

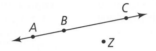

Points A, B, and C are collinear, but points A, B, and Z are noncollinear.

Common difference (p. 148)   The difference between consecutive terms of an arithmetic sequence.

Diferencia común (p. 148)   La diferencia común es la diferencia entre los términos consecutivos de una progresión aritmética.

Example   The common difference is 3 in the arithmetic sequence 4, 7, 10, 13, . . .

Complementary angles (p. 467)   Two angles are complementary angles if the sum of their measures is 90.

Ángulos complementarios (p. 467)   Dos ángulos son complementarios si la suma de sus medidas es igual a 90 grados.

Example

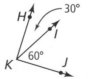

$\angle HKI$ and $\angle IKJ$ are complementary angles, as are $\angle HKI$ and $\angle EFG$.

English

Spanish

Composition of transformations (p. 500)
A composition of two transformations is a transformation in which a second transformation is performed on the image of a first transformation.

Composición de transformaciones (p. 500)
Una composición de dos transformaciones es una transformación en la cual una segunda transformación se realiza a partir de la imagen de la primera.

Example

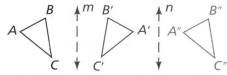

If you reflect $\triangle ABC$ across line m to get $\triangle A'B'C'$ and then reflect $\triangle A'B'C'$ across line n to get $\triangle A''B''C''$, you perform a composition of transformations.

Compound inequality (p. 70) Two inequalities that are joined by *and* or *or*.

Desigualdade compuesta (p. 70) Dos desigualdades que están enlazadas por medio de una *y* o una *o*.

Example $5 < x$ and $x < 10$
$14 < x$ or $x \leq -3$

Compound interest (p. 311) Interest paid on both the principal and the interest that has already been paid.

Interés compuesto (p. 311) Interés calculado tanto sobre el capital como sobre los intereses ya pagados.

Example For an initial deposit of $1000 at a 6% interest rate with interest compounded quarterly, the function $y = 1000\left(\frac{0.06}{4}\right)^{x}$ gives the account balance y after x years.

Conditional relative frequency (p. 418)
Conditional relative frequency is the quotient of a joint frequency in a two-way frequency table and the marginal frequency of the row or column that the joint frequency appears in.

Frecuencia relativa condicionada (p. 418)
Frecuencia relativa condicionada es el cociente de una frecuencia conjunta en una tabla de frecuencias de doble entrada y la frecuencia marginal de la fila o columna en la que la frecuencia conjunta aparece.

Example

	Male	Female	Totals
Juniors	3	4	7
Seniors	3	2	5
Totals	6	6	12

The conditional relative frequency that a student is female given that she is a senior is $\frac{2}{5}$.

English

Spanish

Congruent angles (p. 461) Congruent angles are angles that have the same measure.

Ángulos congruentes (p. 461) Los ángulos congruentes son ángulos que tienen la misma medida.

Example

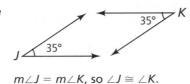

$m\angle J = m\angle K$, so $\angle J \cong \angle K$.

Congruent segments (p. 453) Congruent segments are segments that have the same length.

Segmentos congruentes (p. 453) Los segmentos congruentes son segmentos que tienen la misma longitud.

Example

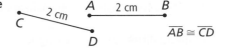

$\overline{AB} \cong \overline{CD}$

Consistent system (p. 233) A system of equations that has at least one solution is consistent.

Sistema consistente (p. 233) Un sistema de ecuaciones que tiene por lo menos una solución es consistente.

Example

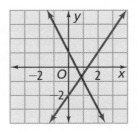

Constant (p. 6) A term that has no variable factor.

Constante (p. 6) Término que tiene un valor fijo.

Example In the expression $4x + 13y + 17$, 17 is a constant term.

Constant of variation for direct variation (p. 176) The nonzero constant k in the function $y = kx$.

Constante de variación en variaciones directas (p. 176) La constante k cuyo valor no es cero en la función $y = kx$.

Example For the direct variation $y = 24x$, 24 is the constant of variation.

Continuous graph (p. 119) A graph that is unbroken.

Gráfica continua (p. 119) Una gráfica continua es una gráfica ininterrumpida.

Example

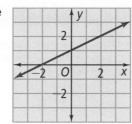

English

Spanish

Conversion factor (p. 38)   A ratio of two equivalent measures in different units.

Factor de conversión (p. 38)   Razón de dos medidas equivalentes en unidades diferentes.

Example   The ratio $\frac{1 \text{ ft}}{12 \text{ in.}}$ is a conversion factor.

Coordinate(s) of a point (p. 451)   The coordinate of a point is its distance and direction from the origin of a number line. The coordinates of a point on a coordinate plane are in the form (x, y), where x is the x-coordinate and y is the y-coordinate.

Coordenada(s) de un punto (p. 451)   La coordenada de un punto es su distancia y dirección desde el origen en una recta numérica. Las coordenadas de un punto en un plano de coordenadas se expresan como (x, y), donde x es la coordenada x, e y es la coordenada y.

Example

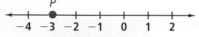

The coordinate of P is -3.

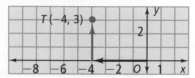

The coordinates of T are $(-4, 3)$.

Coplanar figures (p. 442)   Coplanar figures are figures in the same plane.

Figuras coplanarias (p. 442)   Las figuras coplanarias son las figuras que están localizadas en el mismo plano.

Example

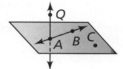

Point C and $\overleftrightarrow{AB}$ are coplanar but points A, B, C, and Q are noncoplanar.

Coplanar points (p. 442)   Coplanar figures are figures in the same plane.

Puntos coplanarios (p. 442)   Las figuras coplanarias son las figuras que están localizadas en el mismo plano.

Correlation coefficient (p. 404)   A number from -1 to 1 that tells you how closely the equation of the line of best fit models the data.

Coeficiente de correlación (p. 404)   Número de 1 a 1 que indica con cuánta exactitud la línea de mejor encaje representa los datos.

Example

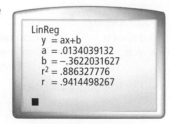

The correlation coefficient is approximately 0.94.

Visual Glossary

Cross products (of a proportion) (p. 53) In a proportion $\frac{a}{b} = \frac{c}{d}$, the products ad and bc. These products are equal.

Productos cruzados (de una proporción) (p. 53) En una proporción $\frac{a}{b} = \frac{c}{d}$, los productos ad y bc. Estos productos son iguales.

Example The cross products for
$\frac{3}{4} = \frac{6}{8}$ are $3 \cdot 8$ and $4 \cdot 6$.

Cube root function (p. 356) A function containing a cube root with the independent variable in the radicand.

Función de la raíz cúbica (p. 356) Una función que contiene una raíz cúbica con la variable independiente en el radicando.

Cumulative frequency table (p. 375) A table that shows the number of data values that lie in or below the given intervals.

Tabla de frecuencia cumulativa (p. 375) Tabla que muestra el número de valores de datos que están dentro o por debajo de los intervalos dados.

Example

Interval	Frequency	Cumulative Frequency
0–9	5	5
10–19	8	13
20–29	4	17

D

Decay factor (p. 312) 1 minus the percent rate of change, expressed as a decimal, for an exponential decay situation.

Factor de decremento (p. 312) 1 menos la tasa porcentual de cambio, expresada como decimal, en una situación de reducción exponencial.

Example The decay factor of the function
$y = 5(0.3)^x$ is 0.3.

Dependent system (p. 233) A system of equations that does not have a unique solution.

Sistema dependiente (p. 233) Sistema de ecuaciones que no tiene una solución única.

Example The system $\begin{cases} y = 2x + 3 \\ -4x + 2y = 6 \end{cases}$ represents two equations for the same line, so it has many solutions. It is a dependent system.

Dependent variable (p. 103) A variable that provides the output values of a function.

Variable dependiente (p. 103) Variable de la que dependen los valores de salida de una función.

Example In the equation $y = 3x$, y is the dependent variable.

Direct variation (p. 176) A linear function defined by an equation of the form $y = kx$, where $k \neq 0$.

Variación directa (p. 176) Una función lineal definida por una ecuación de la forma $y\ kx$, donde $k \neq 0$, representa una variación directa.

Example $y = 18x$ is a direct variation.

English

Spanish

Discrete graph (p. 119) A graph composed of isolated points.

Gráfica discreta (p. 119) Una gráfica discreta es compuesta de puntos aislados.

Example

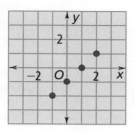

Distance between two points on a line (p. 451) The distance between two points on a line is the absolute value of the difference of the coordinates of the points.

Distancia entre dos puntos de una linea (p. 451) Ladistancia entre dos puntos de una Ifnea es el valor absoluto de la diferencia de las coordenadas de los puntos.

Example

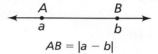

$$AB = |a - b|$$

Distributive Property (p. 3) For every real number a, b, and c:

$a(b + c) = ab + ac$

$(b + c)a = ba + ca$

$a(b - c) = ab - ac$

$(b - c)a = ba - ca$

Propiedad Distributiva (p. 3) Para cada número real a, b y c:

$a(b + c) = ab + ac$

$(b + c)a = ba + ca$

$a(b - c) = ab - ac$

$(b - c)a = ba - ca$

Example $3(19 + 4) = 3(19) + 3(4)$

$(19 + 4)3 = 19(3) + 4(3)$

$7(11 - 2) = 7(11) - 7(2)$

$(11 - 2)7 = 11(7) - 2(7)$

Domain (of a relation or function) (p. 135) The possible values for the input of a relation or function.

Dominio (de una relación o función) (p. 135) Posibles valores de entrada de una relación o función.

Example In the function $f(x) = x + 22$, the domain is all real numbers.

 E

Elimination method (p. 247) A method for solving a system of linear equations. You add or subtract the equations to eliminate a variable.

Eliminación (p. 247) Método para resolver un sistema de ecuaciones lineales. Se suman o se restan las ecuaciones para eliminar una variable.

Example $3x + y = 19$

$\underline{2x - y = 1}$ Add the equations to get $x = 4$.

$5x + 0 = 20$ Substitute 4 for x in

$2(4) - y = 1 \rightarrow$ the second equation.

$8 - y = 1$

$y = 7$ Solve for y.

English

Spanish

Even function (p. 144) A function f is an even function if and only if $f(-x) = f(x)$ for all values of x in its domain.

Función par (p. 144) Una función f es una función par si y solo si $f(-x) = f(x)$ para todos los valores de x en su dominio.

Example $f(x) = x^2 + |x|$ is an even function because $f(-x) = (-x)^2 + |-x| = x^2 + |x| = f(x)$

Explicit formula (p. 150) An explicit formula expresses the nth term of a sequence in terms of n.

Fórmula explícita (p. 150) Una fórmula explícita expresa el n-ésimo término de una progresión en función de n.

Example Let $a_n = 2n + 5$ for positive integers n. If $n = 7$, then $a_7 = 2(7) + 5 = 19$.

Exponential decay (p. 312) A situation modeled with a function of the form $y = ab^x$, where $a > 0$ and $0 < b < 1$.

Decremento exponencial (p. 312) Para $a > 0$ y $0 < b < 1$, la función $y = ab^x$ representa el decremento exponencial.

Example $y = 5(0.1)^x$

Exponential function (p. 291) A function that repeatedly multiplies an initial amount by the same positive number. You can model all exponential functions using $y = ab^x$, where a is a nonzero constant, $b > 0$, and $b \neq 1$.

Función exponencial (p. 291) Función que multiplica repetidas veces una cantidad inicial por el mismo número positivo. Todas las funciones exponenciales se pueden representar mediante $y = ab^x$, donde a es una constante con valor distinto de cero, $b > 0$, y $b \neq 1$.

Example

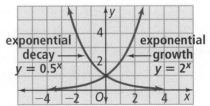

Exponential growth (p. 309) A situation modeled with a function of the form $y = ab^x$, where $a > 0$ and $b > 1$.

Incremento exponencial (p. 309) Para $a > 0$ y $b > 1$, la función $y = ab^x$ representa el incremento exponencial.

Example $y = 100(2)^x$

Extrapolation (p. 401) The process of predicting a value outside the range of known values.

Extrapolación (p. 401) Proceso que se usa para predecir un valor por fuera del ámbito de los valores dados.

Formula (p. 31) An equation that states a relationship among quantities.

Fórmula (p. 31) Ecuación que establece una relación entre cantidades.

Example The formula for the volume V of a cylinder is $V = \pi r^2 h$, where r is the radius of the cylinder and h is its height.

Visual **Glossary**

English

Frequency (p. 371)   The number of data items in an interval.

Frequency table (p. 371)   A table that groups a set of data values into intervals and shows the frequency for each interval.

Example

Interval	Frequency
0–9	5
10–19	8
20–29	4

Function (p. 105)   A relation that assigns exactly one value in the range to each value of the domain.

Example   Earned income is a function of the number of hours worked. If you earn $4.50/h, then your income is expressed by the function $f(h) = 4.5h$.

Function notation (p. 137)   To write a rule in function notation, you use the symbol $f(x)$ in place of y.

Example $f(x) = 3x - 8$ is in function notation.

Geometric sequence (p. 329)   A number sequence formed by multiplying a term in a sequence by a fixed number to find the next term.

Example   9, 3, 1, $\frac{1}{3}$,... is an example of a geometric sequence.

Glide reflection (p. 536)   A glide reflection is the composition of a translation followed by a reflection across a line parallel to the direction of translation.

Example

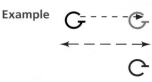

The blue G in the diagram is a glide reflection image of the black G.

Spanish

Frecuencia (p. 371)   Número de datos de un intervalo.

Tabla de frecuencias (p. 371)   Tabla que agrupa un conjunto de datos en intervalos y muestra la frecuencia de cada intervalo.

Función (p. 105)   La relación que asigna exactamente un valor del rango a cada valor del dominio.

Notación de una función (p. 137)   Para expresar una regla en notación de función se usa el símbolo $f(x)$ en lugar de y.

Progresión geométrica (p. 329)   Tipo de sucesión numérica formada al multiplicar un término de la secuencia por un número constante, para hallar el siguiente término.

Reflexión deslizada (p. 536)   Una reflexión por deslizamiento es la composición de una traslación seguida por una reflexión a través de una línea paralela a la dirección de traslación.

English

Spanish

Growth factor (p. 309) 1 plus the percent rate of change for an exponential growth situation.

Factor incremental (p. 309) 1 más la tasa porcentual de cambio en una situación de incremento exponencial.

Example The growth factor of $y = 7(1.3)^x$ is 1.3.

H

Height *See* parallelogram; trapezoid; triangle.

Altura *Ver* parallelogram; trapezoid.

Histogram (p. 372) A special type of bar graph that can display data from a frequency table. Each bar represents an interval. The height of each bar shows the frequency of the interval it represents.

Histograma (p. 372) Tipo de gráfica de barras que muestra los datos de una tabla de frecuencia. Cada barra representa un intervalo. La altura de cada barra muestra la frecuencia del intervalo al que representa.

Example

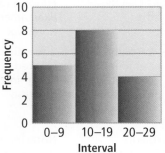

I

Image (p. 495) *See* transformation.

Imagen (p. 495) *Ver* transformation.

Identity (p. 24) An equation that is true for every value.

Identidad (p. 24) Una ecuación que es verdadera para todos los valores.

Example $5 - 14x = 5\left(1 - \frac{14}{5}x\right)$ is an identity because it is true for any value of x.

Inconsistent system (p. 233) A system of equations that has no solution.

Sistema incompatible (p. 233) Un sistema incompatible es un sistema de ecuaciones para el cual no hay solución.

Example $\begin{cases} y = 2x + 3 \\ -2x + y = 1 \end{cases}$ is a system of parallel lines, so it has no solution. It is an inconsistent system.

Independent system (p. 233) A system of linear equations that has a unique solution.

Sistema independiente (p. 233) Un sistema de ecuaciones lineales que tenga una sola solución es un sistema independiente.

Example $\begin{cases} x + 2y = -7 \\ 2x - 3y = 0 \end{cases}$ has the unique solution $(-3, -2)$. It is an independent system.

Visual Glossary

English

Spanish

Independent variable (p. 103) A variable that provides the input values of a function.

Variable independiente (p. 103) Variable de la que dependen los valores de entrada de una función.

Example In the equation $y = 3x$, x is the independent variable.

Input (p. 103) A value of the independent variable.

Entrada (p. 103) Valor de una variable independiente.

Example The input is any value of x you substitute into a function.

Interpolation (p. 401) The process of estimating a value between two known quantities.

Interpolación (p. 401) Proceso que se usa para estimar el valor entre dos cantidades dadas.

Interquartile range (p. 392) The interquartile range of a set of data is the difference between the third and first quartiles.

Intervalo intercuartil (p. 392) El rango intercuartil de un conjunto de datos es la diferencia entre el tercero y el primer cuartiles.

Example The first and third quartiles of the data set 2, 3, 4, 5, 5, 6, 7, and 7 are 3.5 and 6.5. The interquartile range is $6.5 - 3.5 = 3$.

Intersection (p. 444) The intersection of two or more geometric figures is the set of points the figures have in common.

Intersección (p. 444) La intersección de dos o más figuras geométricas es el conjunto de puntos que las figuras tienen en común.

Example

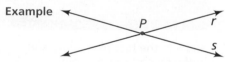

The intersection of lines r and s is point P.

Interval notation (p. 74) A notation for describing an interval on a number line. The interval's endpoint(s) are given, and a parenthesis or bracket is used to indicate whether each endpoint is included in the interval.

Notación de intervalo (p. 74) Notación que describe un intervalo en una recta numérica. Los extremos del intervalo se incluyen y se usa un paréntesis o corchete para indicar si cada extremo está incluido en el intervalo.

Example For $-2 \le x < 8$, the interval notation is $[-2, 8)$.

Isometric drawing (p. 433) An isometric drawing shows a corner view of a three-dimensional figure. It is usually drawn on isometric dot paper. An isometric drawing allows you to see the top, front, and side of an object in the same drawing.

Dibujo isométrico (p. 433) Un dibujo isométrico muestra la perspectiva de una esquina de una figura tridimensional. Generalmente se dibuja en papel punteado isométrico. Un dibujo isométrico permite ver la cima, el frente, y el lado de un objeto en el mismo dibujo.

Example

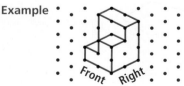

English

Spanish

Isometry (p. 532) An isometry, also known as a *congruence transformation*, is a transformation in which an original figure and its image are congruent.

Isometría (p. 532) Una isometría, conocida también como una *transformación de congruencia*, es una transformación en donde una figura original y su imagen son congruentes.

Example The four isometries are reflections, rotations, translations, and glide reflections.

Isosceles trapezoid (p. 483) An isosceles trapezoid is a trapezoid whose nonparallel sides are congruent.

Trapecio isósceles (p. 483) Un trapecio isósceles es un trapecio cuyos lados opuestos no paralelos son congruentes.

Example

 J

Joint frequency (p. 414) A joint frequency is an entry in the body of a two-way frequency table.

Frecuencia conjunta (p. 414) Una frecuencia conjunta es una entrada en el cuerpo de una tabla de frecuencias de doble entrada.

Example

	Male	Female	Totals
Juniors	3	4	7
Seniors	3	2	5
Totals	6	6	12

3 and 4 in the first row, and 3 and 2 in the second row are joint frequencies.

Joint relative frequency (p. 416) A joint relative frequency is a joint frequency in a two-way frequency table divided by the grand total of table. It is also an entry in the body of a two-way relative frequency table.

Frecuencia relativa conjunta (p. 416) Una frecuencia relativa conjunta es una frecuencia conjunta en una tabla de frecuencias de doble entrada dividido por el total de las entradas de la tabla. Es también una entrada en el cuerpo de una tabla de frecuencias relativas de doble entrada.

K

Kite (p. 483) A kite is a quadrilateral with two pairs of consecutive sides congruent and no opposite sides congruent.

Cometa (p. 483) Una cometa es un cuadrilatero con dos pares de lados congruentes consecutivos y sin laods opuestos congruentes.

Example

Visual Glossary

English

L

Like terms (p. 7)   Terms with exactly the same variable factors in a variable expression.

Example $3\sqrt{7}$ and $25\sqrt{7}$ are like radicals.

Line (p. 441)   In Euclidean geometry, a line is undefined. You can think of a line as a straight path that extends in two opposite directions without end and has no thickness. A line contains infinitely many points. In spherical geometry, you can think of a line as a great circle of a sphere.

Example

Line of best fit (p. 404)   The most accurate trend line on a scatter plot showing the relationship between two sets of data.

Example

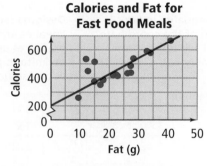

Line of reflection (p. 508)   *See* reflection.

Line of symmetry (p. 523)   *See* reflectional symmetry.

Line plot (p. 382)   A line plot is a graph that shows the shape of a data set by stacking X's above each data value on a number line.

Example

Company A

X   X
X   X   X   X
X   X   X   X   X   X
50   51   52   53   54   55
Monthly Earnings
(thousands of dollars)

Line symmetry (p. 523)   *See* reflectional symmetry.

Spanish

Radicales semejantes (p. 7)   Expresiones radicales con los mismos radicandos.

Recta (p. 441)   En la geometría euclidiana, una recta es indefinida. Se puede pensar en una recta como un camino derecho que se extiende en direcciones opuestas sin fin ni grosor. Una recta tiene un número infinito de puntos. En la geometría esférica, se puede pensar en una recta como un gran círculo de una esfera.

Recta de mayor aproximación (p. 404)   La línea de tendencia en un diagrama de puntos que más se acerca a los puntos que representan la relación entre dos conjuntos de datos.

Eje de reflexión (p. 508)   *Ver* reflection.

Eje de simetría (p. 523)   *Ver* reflectional symmetry.

Diagrama de puntos (p. 382)   Un diagrama de puntos es una gráfica que muestra la forma de un conjunto de datos agrupando X sobre cada valor de una recta numérica.

Simetría axial (p. 523)   *Ver* reflectional symmetry.

English

Spanish

Linear equation (p. 186)   An equation whose graph forms a straight line.

Ecuación lineal (p. 186)   Ecuación cuya gráfica es una línea recta.

Example
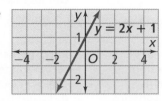

Linear function (p. 105)   A function whose graph is a line is a linear function. You can represent a linear function with a linear equation.

Función lineal (p. 105)   Una función cuya gráfica es una recta es una función lineal. La función lineal se representa con una ecuación lineal.

Example
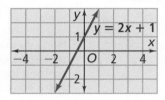

Linear inequality (p. 263)   An inequality in two variables whose graph is a region of the coordinate plane that is bounded by a line. Each point in the region is a solution of the inequality.

Desigualdad lineal (p. 263)   Una desigualdad lineal es una desigualdad de dos variables cuya gráfica es una región del plano de coordenadas delimitado por una recta. Cada punto de la región es una solución de la desigualdad.

Example
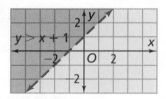

Linear pair (p. 469)   A linear pair is a pair of adjacent angles whose noncommon sides are opposite rays.

Par lineal (p. 469)   Un par lineal es un par de ángulos adjuntos cuyos lados no comunes son semirrectas opuestas.

Example
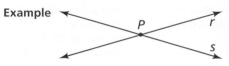
The intersection of lines r and s is point P.

Linear parent function (p. 186)   The simplest form of a linear function.

Función lineal elemental (p. 186)   La forma más simple de una función lineal.

Example $y = x$

Literal equation (p. 29)   An equation involving two or more variables.

Ecuación literal (p. 29)   Ecuación que incluye dos o más variables.

Example $4x + 2y = 18$ is a literal equation.

English

Marginal frequency (p. 414)   A marginal frequency is an entry in the Total row or Total column of a two-way frequency table.

Example

	Male	Female	Totals
Juniors	3	4	7
Seniors	3	2	5
Totals	6	6	12

6 and 6 in the Total row and 7 and 5 in the Total column are marginal frequencies.

Marginal relative frequency (p. 416)   A marginal relative frequency is a marginal frequency in a two-way frequency table divided by the grand total for the table.

Mean (p. 379)   To find the mean of a set of data values, find the sum of the data values and divide the sum by the number of data values. The mean is $\frac{\text{sum of the data values}}{\text{total number of data values}}$.

Example   In the data set 12, 11, 12, 10, 13, 12, and 7, the mean is $\frac{12 + 11 + 12 + 10 + 13 + 12 + 7}{7} = 11$

Mean absolute deviation (MAD) (p. 388)   Mean absolute deviation is a measure of the spread of a data set. For data values $x_1, x_2, \ldots, x_n$, the mean absolute deviation is given by $\frac{|x_1 - \bar{x}| + |x_2 - \bar{x}| + \ldots + |x_n - \bar{x}|}{n}$, where $\bar{x}$ is the mean of the data set.

Measure of an angle (p. 460)   Consider $\overrightarrow{OD}$ and a point C on one side of $\overrightarrow{OD}$. Every ray of the form $\overrightarrow{OC}$ can be paired one to one with a real number from 0 to 180. The measure of $\angle COD$ is the absolute value of the difference of the real numbers paired with $\overrightarrow{OC}$ and $\overrightarrow{OD}$.

Example

$m\angle COD = 105$

Spanish

Frecuencia marginal (p. 414)   Una frecuencia marginal es una entrada en la fila Total o columna Total de una tabla de frecuencias de doble entrada.

Frecuencia relativa marginal (p. 416)   Una frecuencia relativa marginal es una frecuencia marginal en una tabla de frecuencias de doble entrada dividido por el total de la tabla.

Media (p. 379)   Para hallar la media de un conjunto de datos, halla la suma de los valores de los datos y divide la suma por el total del valor de los datos. La media es $\frac{\text{la suma de los datos}}{\text{el número total de valores de datos}}$.

Desviación absoluta media (p. 388)   Desviación absoluta media es una medida de la dispersión de un conjunto de datos. Para los datos $x_1, x_2, \ldots, x_n$, la desviación absoluta media es igual a $\frac{|x_1 - \bar{x}| + |x_2 - \bar{x}| + \ldots + |x_n - \bar{x}|}{n}$, donde $\bar{x}$ es la media del conjunto de datos.

Medida de un ángulo (p. 460)   Toma en cuenta $\overrightarrow{OD}$ y un punto C a un lado de $\overrightarrow{OD}$. Cada semirrecta de la forma $\overrightarrow{OC}$ puede ser emparejada exactamente con un número real de 0 a 180. La medida de $\angle COD$ es el valor absoluto de la diferencia de los números reales emparejados con $\overrightarrow{OC}$ y $\overrightarrow{OD}$.

English	Spanish
Measure of central tendency (p. 379) Mean, median, and mode. They are used to organize and summarize a set of data.	**Medida de tendencia central (p. 379)** La media, la mediana y la moda. Se usan para organizar y resumir un conjunto de datos.

Example For examples, see *mean*, *median*, and *mode*.

Measure of dispersion (p. 382) A measure that describes how dispersed, or spread out, the values in a data set are. Range is a measure of dispersion.	**Medida de dispersión (p. 382)** Medida que describe cómo se dispersan, o esparecen, los valores de un conjunto de datos. La amplitud es una medida de dispersión.

Example For an example, see *range*.

Median (p. 379) The middle value in an ordered set of numbers.	**Mediana (p. 379)** El valor del medio en un conjunto ordenado de números.

Example In the data set 7, 10, 11, 12, 12, 12, and 13, the median is 12.

Midpoint of a segment (p. 454) A midpoint of a segment is the point that divides the segment into two congruent segments.	**Punto medio de un segmento (p. 454)** El punto medio de un segmento es el punto que divide el segmento en dos segmentos congruentes.

Example

Midpoint of $\overline{AB}$

A   M   B

Mode (p. 379) The mode is the most frequently occurring value (or values) in a set of data. A data set may have no mode, one mode, or more than one mode.	**Moda (p. 379)** La moda es el valor o valores que ocurren con mayor frequencia en un conjunto de datos. El conjunto de datos puede no tener moda, o tener una o más modas.

Example In the data set 7, 7, 9, 10, 11, and 13, the mode is 7.

N

Negative correlation (p. 399) The relationship between two sets of data, in which one set of data decreases as the other set of data increases.	**Correlación negativa (p. 399)** Relación entre dos conjuntos de datos en la que uno de los conjuntos disminuye a medida que el otro aumenta.

Example

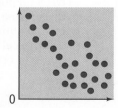

English

Spanish

Net (p. 431)   A net is a two-dimensional pattern that you can fold to form a three-dimensional figure.

Plantilla (p. 431)   Una plantilla es una figura bidimensional que se puede doblar para formar una figura tridimensional.

Example

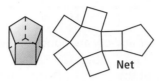

The net shown can be folded into a prism with pentagonal bases.

No correlation (p. 399)   There does not appear to be a relationship between two sets of data.

Sin correlación (p. 399)   No hay relación entre dos conjuntos de datos.

Example

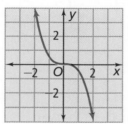

Nonlinear function (p. 110)   A function whose graph is not a line or part of a line.

Función no lineal (p. 110)   Función cuya gráfica no es una línea o parte de una línea.

Example

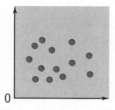

O

Obtuse angle (p. 460)   An obtuse angle is an angle whose measure is between 90 and 180.

Ángulo obtuso (p. 460)   Un ángulo obtuso es un ángulo que mide entre 90 y 180 grados.

Example

147°

Odd function (p. 144)   A function f is an odd function if and only if $f(-x) = -f(x)$ for all values of x in its domain.

Función impar (p. 144)   Una función f es una función impar si y solo si $f(-x) = -f(x)$ para todos los valores de x en su dominio.

Example   The function $f(x) = x^3 + 2x$ is odd because $f(-x) = (-x)^3 + 2(-x) = -x^3 - 2x = -f(x)$

English

Spanish

Opposite rays (p. 443) Opposite rays are collinear rays with the same endpoint. They form a line.

Semirrectas opuestas (p. 443) Las semirrectas opuestos son semirrectas colineales con el mismo extremo. Forman una recta.

Example

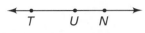

$\overrightarrow{UT}$ and $\overrightarrow{UN}$ are opposite rays.

Opposite reciprocals (p. 214) A number of the form $-\frac{b}{a}$, where $\frac{a}{b}$ is a nonzero rational number. The product of a number and its opposite reciprocal is -1.

Recíproco inverso (p. 214) Número en la forma $-\frac{b}{a}$, donde $\frac{a}{b}$ es un número racional diferente de cero. El producto de un número y su recíproco inverso es -1.

Example $\frac{2}{5}$ and $-\frac{5}{2}$ are opposite reciprocals because $\left(\frac{2}{5}\right)\left(-\frac{5}{2}\right) = -1$.

Orthographic drawing (p. 435) An orthographic drawing is the top view, front view, and right-side view of a three-dimensional figure.

Dibujo ortográfico (p. 435) Un dibujo ortográfico es la vista desde arriba, la vista de frente y la vista del lado derecho de una figura tridimensional.

Example The diagram shows an isometric drawing (upper right) and the three views that make up an orthographic drawing.

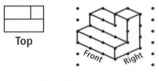

Outlier (p. 379) An outlier is a data value that is much higher or lower than the other data values in the set.

Valor extremo (p. 379) Un valor extremo es el valor de un dato que es mucho más alto o mucho más bajo que los otros valores del conjunto de datos.

Example For the set of values 2, 5, 3, 7, 12, the data value 12 is an outlier.

Output (p. 103) A value of the dependent variable.

Salida (p. 103) Valor de una variable dependiente.

Example The output of the function $f(x) = x^2$ when $x = 3$ is 9.

English

P

Parallel lines (p. 212)   Two lines are parallel if they lie in the same plane and do not intersect. The symbol ∥ means "is parallel to".

Example $\ell \parallel m$

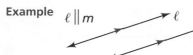

Parallelogram (p. 483)   A parallelogram is a quadrilateral with two pairs of parallel sides. You can choose any side to be the *base*. An *altitude* is any segment perpendicular to the line containing the base drawn from the side opposite the base. The *height* is the length of an altitude.

Example

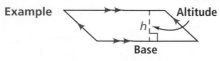

Altitude

h

Base

Parent function (p. 186)   A family of functions is a group of functions with common characteristics. A parent function is the simplest function with these characteristics.

Example $y = x$ is the parent function for the family of linear equations of the form $y = mx + b$.

Percentile (p. 395)   A value that separates a data set into 100 equal parts.

Percentile rank (p. 395)   The percentage of data values that are less than or equal to a given value.

Perimeter of a polygon (p. 545)   The perimeter of a polygon is the sum of the lengths of its sides.

Example

4 in.

4 in.   3 in.

5 in.

$P = 4 + 4 + 5 + 3$
$= 16$ in.

Spanish

Paralle lines (p. 212)   Dos rectas son paralelas si están en el mismo plano y no se cortan. El símbolo ∥ significa "es paralelo a".

The red symbols indicate parallel lines.

Paralelogramo (p. 483)   Un paralelogramo es un cuadrilátero con dos pares de lados paralelos. Se puede escoger cualquier lado como la *base*. Una *altura* es un segmento perpendicular a la recta que contiene la base, trazada desde el lado opuesto a la base. La *altura*, por extensión, es la longitud de una altura.

Función elemental (p. 186)   Una familia de funciones es un grupo de funciones con características en común. La función elemental es la función más simple que reúne esas características.

Percentil (p. 395)   Valor que separa el conjunto de datos en 100 partes iguales.

Rango percentil (p. 395)   Porcentaje de valores de datos que es menos o igual a un valor dado.

Perímetro de un polígono (p. 545)   El perímetro de un polígono es la suma de las longitudes de sus lados.

Visual **Glossary**

Perpendicular lines (p. 213)   Perpendicular lines are lines that intersect and form right angles. The symbol ⊥ means "is perpendicular to".

Rectas Perpendiculars (p. 213)   Las rectas perpendiculars son recta sue se cortan y frman angulos rectos. El símbolo ⊥ significa "es perpendicular a".

Example

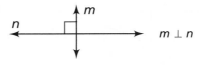

$m \perp n$

Piecewise function (p. 357)   A piecewise function has different rules for different parts of its domain.

Función de fragmentos (p. 357)   Una función de fragmentos tiene reglas diferentes para diferentes partes de su dominio.

Plane (p. 441)   In Euclidean geometry, a plane is undefined. You can think of a plane as a flat surface that extends without end and has no thickness. A plane contains infinitely many lines.

Plano (p. 441)   En la geometría euclidiana, un plano es indefinido. Se puede pensar en un plano como una superficie plana sin fin, ni grosor. Un plano tiene un número infinito de rectas.

Example

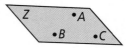

Plane *ABC* or plane *Z*

Point (p. 441)   In Euclidean geometry, a point is undefined. You can think of a point as a location. A point has no size.

Punto (p. 441)   En la geometría euclidiana, un punto es indefinido. Puedes imaginarte a un punto como un lugar. Un punto no tiene dimensión.

Example • *P*

Point-slope form (p. 195)   A linear equation of a nonvertical line written as $y - y_1 = m(x - x_1)$. The line passes through the point (x_1, y_1) with slope m.

Forma punto-pendiente (p. 195)   La ecuación lineal de una recta no vertical que pasa por el punto (x_1, y_1) con pendiente m está dada por $y - y_1 = m(x - x_1)$.

Example   An equation with a slope of $-\frac{1}{2}$ passing through $(2, -1)$ would be written $y + 1 = -\frac{1}{2}(x - 2)$ in point-slope form.

Point symmetry (p. 523)   Point symmetry is the type of symmetry for which there is a rotation of 180° that maps a figure onto itself.

Simetría central (p. 523)   La simetría central es un tipo de simetría en la que una figura se ha rotado 180° sobre sí misma.

Polygon (p. 483)   A polygon is a closed plane figure formed by three or more segments. Each segment intersects exactly two other segments, but only at their endpoints, and no two segments with a common endpoint are collinear. The *vertices* of the polygon are the endpoints of the sides. A *diagonal* is a segment that connects two non-consecutive vertices.

Polígono (p. 483)   Un polígono es una figura plana compuesta or tres o más semgentos. Cada segmento intersecta los otros dos segments exactamente, pero únicamente en sus puntos extremos y ningúno de los segmentos extremos comunes son colineales. Los *vértices* del polígono son los extremos de los lados. Una *diagonal* es un segmento que conecta dos vértices no consecutivos.

Example

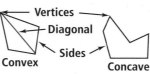

English

Spanish

Positive correlation (p. 399)   The relationship between two sets of data in which both sets of data increase together.

Correlación positiva (p. 399)   La relación entre dos conjuntos de datos en la que ambos conjuntos incrementan a la vez.

Example

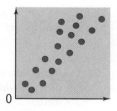

Postulate (p. 444)   A postulate, or *axiom*, is an accepted statement of fact.

Postulado (p. 444)   Un postulado, o *axioma*, es un enunciado que se acepta como un hecho.

Example   Through any two points there is exactly one line.

Preimage (p. 495)   *See* **transformation**.

Preimagen (p. 495)   *Ver* **transformation**.

Proportion (p. 52)   An equation that states that two ratios are equal.

Proporción (p. 52)   Es una ecuación que establece que dos razones son iguales.

Example $\frac{7.5}{9} = \frac{5}{6}$

Q

Quadrilateral (p. 483)   A quadrilateral is a polygon with four sides.

Cuadrilátero (p. 483)   Un cuadrilátero es un polígono de cuatro lados.

Example

Quartile (p. 392)   A quartile is a value that separates a finite data set into four equal parts. The second quartile (Q_2) is the median of the data set. The first and third quartiles (Q_1 and Q_3) are the medians of the lower half and upper half of the data, respectively.

Cuartil (p. 392)   Un cuartil es el valor que separa un conjunto de datos finitos en cuatro partes iguales. El segundo cuartil (Q_2) es la mediana del conjunto de datos. El primer cuartil y el tercer cuartil (Q_1 y Q_3) son medianas de la mitad inferior y de la mitad superior de los datos, respectivamente.

Example   For the data set 2, 3, 4, 5, 5, 6, 7, 7, the first quartile is 3.5, the second quartile (or median) is 5, and the third quartile is 6.5.

R

Radical expression (p. 344)   Expression that contains a radical.

Expresión radical (p. 344)   Expresiones que contienen radicales.

Example $\sqrt{3}$, $\sqrt{5x}$, and $\sqrt{x-10}$ are examples of radical expressions.

English

Range (of a relation or function) (p. 135) The possible values of the output, or dependent variable, of a relation or function.

Example In the function $y = |x|$, the range is the set of all nonnegative numbers.

Range of a set of data (p. 382) The difference between the greatest and the least data values for a set of data.

Example For the set 2, 5, 8, 12, the range is $12 - 2 = 10$.

Rate (p. 37) A ratio of a to b where a and b represent quantities measured in different units.

Example Traveling 125 miles in 2 hours results in the rate $\frac{125 \text{ miles}}{2 \text{ hours}}$ or 62.5 mi/h.

Rate of change (p. 167) The relationship between two quantities that are changing. The rate of change is also called slope.

$\text{rate of change} = \frac{\text{change in the dependent variable}}{\text{change in the independent variable}}$

Example Video rental for 1 day is $1.99. Video rental for 2 days is $2.99.

$\text{rate of change} = \frac{2.99 - 1.99}{2 - 1}$
$= \frac{1.00}{1}$
$= 1$

Ratio (p. 37) A ratio is the comparison of two quantities by division.

Example $\frac{5}{7}$ and 7 : 3 are ratios.

Rationalize the denominator (p. 349) To rationalize the denominator of an expression, rewrite it so there are no radicals in any denominator and no denominators in any radical.

Example $\frac{2}{\sqrt{5}} = \frac{2}{\sqrt{5}} \cdot \frac{\sqrt{5}}{\sqrt{5}} = \frac{2\sqrt{5}}{\sqrt{25}} = \frac{2\sqrt{5}}{5}$

Ray (p. 443) A ray is the part of a line that consists of one *endpoint* and all the points of the line on one side of the endpoint.

Example

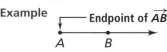

Spanish

Rango (de una relación o función) (p. 135) El conjunto de todos los valores posibles de la salida, o variable dependiente, de una relación o función.

Rango de un conjunto de datos (p. 382) Diferencia entre el valor mayor y el menor en un conjunto de datos.

Tasa (p. 37) La relación que existe entre a y b cuando a y b son cantidades medidas con distintas unidades.

Tasa de cambio (p. 167) La relación entre dos cantidades que cambian. La tasa de cambio se llama también pendiente.

$\text{tasa de cambio} = \frac{\text{cambio en la variable dependiente}}{\text{cambio en la variable independiente}}$

Razón (p. 37) Una razón es la comparación de dos cantidades por medio de una división.

Racionalizar el denominador (p. 349) Para racionalizar el denominador de una expresión, ésta se escribe de modo que no haya radicales en ningún denominador y no haya denominadores en ningún radical.

Semirrecta (p. 443) Una semirrecta es la parte de una recta que tiene un *extremo* de donde parten todos los puntos de la recta.

English

Spanish

Rectangle (p. 483) A rectangle is a parallelogram with four right angles.

Rectangle (p. 483) Un rectángulo es un paralelogramo con cuatro ángulos rectos.

Example

Recursive formula (p. 149) A recursive formula defines the terms in a sequence by relating each term to the ones before it.

Fórmula recursiva (p. 149) Una fórmula recursiva define los términos de una secuencia al relacionar cada término con los términos que lo anteceden.

Example Let $a_n = 2.5a_{n-1} + 3a_{n-2}$. If $a_5 = 3$ and $a_4 = 7.5$, then
$a_6 = 2.5(3) + 3(7.5) = 30$.

Reflection (p. 508) A reflection (*flip*) across line r, called the *line of reflection*, is a transformation such that if a point A is on line r, then the image of A is itself, and if a point B is not on line r, then its image B' is the point such that r is the perpendicular bisector of $\overline{BB'}$.

Reflexión (p. 508) Una reflexión (*inversión*) a través de una línea r, llamada el *eje de reflexión*, es una transformación en la que si un punto A es parte de la línea r, la imagen de A es sí misma, y si un punto B no está en la línea r, su imagen B' es el punto en el cual la línea r es la bisectriz perpendicular de $\overline{BB'}$.

Example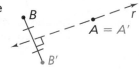

Reflectional symmetry (p. 523) Reflectional symmetry, or *line symmetry*, is the type of symmetry for which there is a reflection that maps a figure onto itself. The reflection line is the line of symmetry. The *line of symmetry* divides a figure with reflectional symmetry into two congruent halves.

Simetría reflexiva (p. 523) Simetría reflexiva, o *simetría lineal*, es el tipo de simetría donde hay una reflexión que ubica una figura en sí misma. El eje de reflexión es el *eje de simetría*. El eje de simetría divide una figura con simetría reflexiva en dos mitades congruentes.

Example

A reflection across the given line maps the figure onto itself.

Regular polygon (p. 484) A regular polygon is a polygon that is both equilateral and equiangular. Its *center* is the point that is equidistant from its vertices.

Polígono regular (p. 484) Un polígono regular es un polígono que es equilateral y equiangular. Su *centro* es el punto equidistante de sus vértices.

Example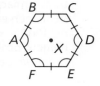

ABCDEF is a regular hexagon. Point *X* is its center.

Relation (p. 135)   Any set of ordered pairs.

Relación (p. 135)   Cualquier conjunto de pares ordenados.

Example   {(0, 0), (2, 3), (2, −7)} is a relation.

Relative frequency (p. 416)   The ratio of the number of times an event occurs to the total number of events in the sample space.

Freuencia relativa (p. 416)   La razón del número de veces que ocurre un evento número de eventos en el espacio muestral.

Example

Archery Results					
Scoring Region	Yellow	Red	Blue	Black	White
Arrow Strikes	52	25	10	8	5

$$\text{Relative frequency of spinning } 1 = \frac{\text{frequency of spinning } 1}{\text{tatal frequencies}}$$
$$= \frac{29}{100}$$

Residual (p. 411)   The difference between the *y*-value of a data point and the corresponding *y*-value of a model for the data set.

Residuo (p. 411)   La diferencia entre el valor de *y* de un punto *y* el valor de y correspondiente a ese punto en el modelo del conjunto de datos.

Rhombus (p. 483)   A rhombus is a parallelogram with four congruent sides.

Rombo (p. 483)   Un rombo es un paralelogramo de cuatro lados congruentes.

Example

Right angle (p. 460)   A right angle is an angle whose measure is 90.

Ángulo recto (p. 460)   Un ángulo recto es un ángulo que mide 90.

Example
90°

This symbol indicates a right angle.

Rigid motion (p. 495)   A transformation in the plane that preserves distance and angle measure.

Movimiento rígido (p. 495)   Una transformación en el piano que no cambia la distancia ni la medida del ángulo.

Example   Translations, reflections, and rotations are rigid motions.

Rotation (p. 515)   A rotation (*turn*) of *x*° about a point *R*, called the *center of rotation*, is a transformation such that for any point *V*, its image is the point *V*′, where $RV = RV'$ and $m\angle VRV' = x$. The image of *R* is itself. The positive number of degrees *x* that a figure rotates is the *angle of rotation*.

Rotación (p. 515)   Una rotación (*giro*) de *x*° sobre un punto *R*, llamado el *centro de rotación*, es una transformación en la que para cualquier punto *V*, su imagen es el punto *V*′, donde $RV = RV'$ y $m\angle VRV' = x$. La imagen de *R* es sí misma. El número positivo de grados *x* que una figura rota es el *ángulo de rotación*.

Example

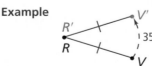

English

Spanish

Rotational symmetry (p. 523) Rotational symmetry is the type of symmetry for which there is a rotation of 180° or less that maps a figure onto itself.

Simetría rotacional (p. 523) La simetría rotacional es un tipo de simetría en la que una rotación de 180° o menos vuelve a trazar una figura sobre sí misma.

Example

The figure has 120° rotational symmetry.

S

Scatter plot (p. 399) A graph that relates two different sets of data by displaying them as ordered pairs.

Diagrama de puntos (p. 399) Grafica que muestra la relacion entre dos conjuntos. Los datos de ambos conjuntos se presentan como pares ordenados.

Example

The scatter plot displays the amount spent on advertising (in thousands of dollars) versus product sales (in millions of dollars).

Segment (p. 443) A segment is the part of a line that consists of two points, called *endpoints*, and all points between them.

Segmento (p. 443) Un segmento es la parte de una recta que tiene dos puntos, llamados *extremos*, entre los cuales están todos los puntos de esa recta.

Example

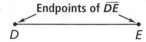

Segment bisector (p. 454) A segment bisector is a line, segment, ray, or plane that intersects a segment at its midpoint.

Bisectriz de un segmento (p. 454) La bisectriz de un segmento es una recta, segmento, semirrecta o plano que corta un segmento en su punto medio.

Example

ℓ bisects $\overline{KJ}$.

Sequence (p. 146) An ordered list of numbers that often forms a pattern.

Progresion (p. 146) Lista ordenada de numeros que muchas veces forma un patron.

Example −4, 5, 14, 23 is a sequence.

Side *See* angle.

Lado *Ver* angle.

English

Spanish

Slope (p. 168) The ratio of the vertical change to the horizontal change.

$$\text{slope} = \frac{\text{vertical change}}{\text{horizontal change}} = \frac{y_2 - y_1}{x_2 - x_1}, \text{ where}$$

$x_2 - x_1 \neq 0$

Pendiente (p. 168) La razón del cambio vertical al cambio horizontal. pendiente cambio vertical cambio horizontal.

$$\text{pendiente} = \frac{\text{cambio vertical}}{\text{cambio horizontal}} = \frac{y_2 - y_1}{x_2 - x_1}, \text{ donde}$$

$x_2 - x_1 \neq 0$

Example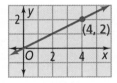

The slope of the line above is $\frac{2}{4} = \frac{1}{2}$.

Slope-intercept form (p. 186) The slope-intercept form of a linear equation is $y = mx + b$, *where m is the slope of the line and b is the y-intercept.*

Forma pendiente-intercepto (p. 186) La forma pendiente-intercepto es la ecuación lineal $y = mx + b$, en la que *m* es la pendiente de la recta y *b* es el punto de intersección de esa recta con el eje *y*.

Example $y = 8x - 2$

Solution of a system of linear equations (p. 231) Any ordered pair in a system that makes all the equations of that system true.

Solución de un sistema de ecuaciones lineales (p. 231) Todo par ordenado de un sistema que hace verdaderas todas las ecuaciones de ese sistema.

Example   (2, 1) is a solution of the system
$y = 2x - 3$
$y = x - 1$
because the ordered pair makes both equations true.

Solution of a system of linear inequalities (p. 271) Any ordered pair that makes all of the inequalities in the system true.

Solución de un sistema de desigualdades lineales (p. 271) Todo par ordenado que hace verdaderas todas las desigualdades del sistema.

Example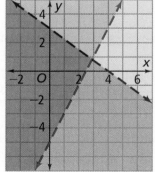

The dark shaded area shows the solution of the system $y > 2x - 5$
$3x + 4y < 12$.

English

Spanish

Solution of an inequality (two variables) (p. 263)   Any ordered pair that makes the inequality true.

Solución de una desigualdad (dos variables) (p. 263)   Cualquier par ordenado que haga verdadera la desigualdad.

Example   Each ordered pair in the shaded area and on the solid red line is a solution of $3x - 5y \le 10$.

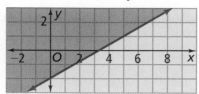

Space (p. 443)   Space is the set of all points.

Espacio (p. 443)   El espacio es el conjunto de todos los puntos.

Square (p. 483)   A square is a parallelogram with four congruent sides and four right angles.

Cuadrado (p. 483)   Un cuadrado es un paralelogramo con cuatro lados congruentes y cuatro ángulos rectos.

Example

Square root function (p. 354)   A function that contains the independent variable in the radicand.

Función de raíz cuadrada (p. 354)   Una función que contiene la variable independiente en el radicando.

Example $y = \sqrt{2x}$ is a square root function.

Standard deviation (p. 390)   A measure of how data varies, or deviates, from the mean.

Desviación típica (p. 390)   Medida de cómo los datos varían, o se desvían, de la media.

Example   Use the following formula to find the standard deviation.

$$\sigma = \sqrt{\frac{\Sigma(x - \bar{x})^2}{n}}$$

Standard form of a linear equation (p. 203)   The standard form of a linear equation is $Ax + By = C$, where A, B, and C are real numbers and A and B are not both zero.

Forma normal de una ecuación lineal (p. 203)   La forma normal de una ecuación lineal es $Ax\ By\ C$, donde A, B y C son números reales, y donde A y B no son iguales a cero.

Example $6x - y = 12$

Step function (p. 358)   A step function pairs every number in an interval with a single value. The graph of a step function can look like the steps of a staircase.

Función escalón (p. 358)   Una función escalón empareja cada número de un intervalo con un solo valor. La gráfica de una función escalón se puede parecer a los peldaños de una escalera.

English

Spanish

Straight angle (p. 460)   A straight angle is an angle whose measure is 180.

Ángulo llano (p. 460)   Un ángulo llano es un ángulo que mide 180.

Example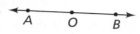

$$m\angle AOB = 180$$

Substitution method (p. 240)   A method of solving a system of equations by replacing one variable with an equivalent expression containing the other variable.

Método de sustitución (p. 240)   Método para resolver un sistema de ecuaciones en el que se reemplaza una variable por una expresión equivalente que contenga la otra variable.

Example   If $y = 2x + 5$ and $x + 3y = 7$, then $x + 3(2x + 5) = 7$.

Supplementary angles (p. 467)   Two angles are supplementary if the sum of their measures is 180.

Ángulos suplementarios (p. 467)   Dos ángulos son suplementarios cuando sus medidas suman 180.

Example

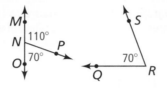

∠MNP and ∠ONP are supplementary, as are ∠MNP and ∠QRS.

Symmetry (p. 523)   A figure has symmetry if there is an isometry that maps the figure onto itself. *See also***point symmetry; reflectional symmetry; rotational symmetry**.

Simetría (p. 523)   Una figura tiene simetría si hay una isometría que traza la figura sobre sí misma. *Ver también***point symmetry; reflectional symmetry; rotational symmetry**.

Example

A regular pentagon has reflectional symmetry and 72° rotational symmetry.

System of linear equations (p. 231)   Two or more linear equations using the same variables.

Sistema de ecuaciones lineales (p. 231)   Dos o más ecuaciones lineales que usen las mismas variables.

Example $y = 5x + 7$
$y = \frac{1}{2}x - 3$

System of linear inequalities (p. 271)   Two or more linear inequalities using the same variables.

Sistema de desigualdades lineales (p. 271)   Dos o más desigualdades lineales que usen las mismas variables.

Example $y \leq x + 11$
$y < 5x$

Term (p. 6)   A number, variable, or the product or quotient of a number and one or more variables.

Término (p. 6)   Un número, una variable o el producto o cociente de un número y una o más variables.

Example   The expression $5x + \frac{y}{2} - 8$ has

three terms: $5x$, $\frac{y}{2}$, and -8.

Term of a sequence (p. 146)   A term of a sequence is any number in a sequence.

Término de una progresión (p. 146)   Un término de una secuencia es cualquier número de una secuencia.

Example -4 is the first term of the sequence -4, 5, 14, 23.

Transformation (p. 495)   A transformation is a change in the position, size, or shape of a geometric figure. The given figure is called the *preimage* and the resulting figure is called the *image*. A transformation *maps* a figure onto its image. *Prime notation* is sometimes used to identify image points. In the diagram, X′ (read "X prime") is the image of X.

Transformación (p. 495)   Una transformación es un cambio en la posición, tamaño o forma de una figura. La figura dada se llama la preimagen y la figura resultante se llama la *imagen*. Una transformación *traza* la figura sobre su propia imagen. La *notación prima* a veces se utilize para identificar los puntos de la imagen. En el diagrama de la derecha, X′ (leído X prima) es la imagen de X.

Example

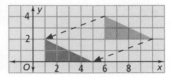

$$\triangle XYZ \rightarrow \triangle X'Y'Z'$$

Translation of a graph (p. 219)   A translation (*slide*) is a transformation that moves points the same distance and in the same direction.

Traslación (p. 219)   Una traslación (*desplazamiento*) es una transformación en la que se mueven puntos la misma distancia en la misma dirección.

Example

The blue triangle is the image of the red triangle under the translation $(-5, -2)$.

Translation (p. 498)   A translation is a transformation that moves points the same distance and in the same direction.

Traslación (p. 498)   Una traslación es una transformación en la que se mueven puntos la misma distancia en la misma dirección.

Example

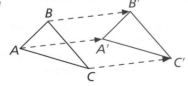

English

Spanish

Trapezoid (p. 483)   A trapezoid is a quadrilateral with exactly one pair of parallel sides, the *bases*. The nonparallel sides are called the *legs* of the trapezoid. Each pair of angles adjacent to a base are *base angles* of the trapezoid. An *altitude* of a trapezoid is a perpendicular segment from one base to the line containing the other base. Its length is called the *height* of the trapezoid.

Trapecio (p. 483)   Un trapecio es un cuadrilátero con exactamente un par de lados paralelos, las *bases*. Los lados no paralelos se llaman los *catetos* del trapecio. Cada par de ángulos adyacentes a la base son los *ángulos de base* del trapecio. Una *altura* del trapecio es un segmento perpendicular que va de una base a la recta que contiene la otra base. Su longitud se llama, por extensión, la *altura* del trapecio.

Example

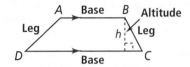

In trapezoid $ABCD$, $\angle ADC$ and $\angle BCD$ are one pair of base angles, and $\angle DAB$ and $\angle ABC$ are the other.

Trend line (p. 401)   A line on a scatter plot drawn near the points. It shows a correlation.

Línea de tendencia (p. 401)   Línea de un diagrama de puntos que se traza cerca de los puntos para mostrar una correlación.

Example

Positive   Negative

Two-way frequency table (p. 414)   A table that displays frequencies in two different categories.

Table de frecuencias de doble entrada (p. 414)   Una tabla de frecuencies que contiene dos categorias de datos.

Example

	Male	Female	Totals
Juniors	3	4	7
Seniors	3	2	5
Totals	6	6	12

Two-way relative frequency table (p. 416)   A two-way relative frequency table shows joint relative frequencies and marginal relative frequencies for two categories of data.

Tabla de frecuencias relativas de doble entrada (p. 416)   Una tabla de frecuencias relativas de doble entrada muestra las frecuencias relativas conjuntas y las frecuencias relativas marginales para dos categorías de datos.

Unit analysis (p. 39)   Including units for each quantity in a calculation to determine the unit of the answer.

Análisis de unidades (p. 39)   Incluir unidades para cada cantidad de un cálculo como ayuda para determinar la unidad que se debe usar para la respuesta.

Example   To change 10 ft to yards, multiply by the conversion factor $\frac{1 \text{ yd}}{3 \text{ ft}}$.

$$10 \text{ ft} \left(\frac{1 \text{ yd}}{3 \text{ ft}}\right) = 3\frac{1}{3} \text{ yd}$$

Visual Glossary

English

Spanish

Unit rate (p. 37)   A rate with a denominator of 1.

Razón en unidades (p. 37)   Razón cuyo denominador es 1.

Example   The unit rate for 120 miles driven in 2 hours is 60 mi/h.

Vertex   *See* angle. The plural form of *vertex* is *vertices*.

Vértice   *Ver* angle.

Vertical angles (p. 466)   Vertical angles are two angles whose sides form two pairs of opposite rays.

Ángulos opuestos por el vértice (p. 466)   Dos ángulos son ángulos opuestos por el vértice si sus lados son semirrectas opuestas.

Example

∠1 and ∠2 are vertical angles, as are ∠3 and ∠4.

Vertical line test (p. 136)   The vertical-line test is a method used to determine if a relation is a function or not. If a vertical line passes through a graph more than once, the graph is not the graph of a function.

Prueba de la recta vertical (p. 136)   La prueba de recta vertical es un método que se usa para determinar si una relación es una función o no. Si una recta vertical pasa por el medio de una gráfica más de una vez, la gráfica no es una gráfica de una función.

Example

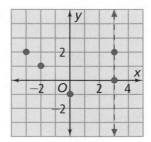

A line would pass through (3, 0) and (3, 2), so the relation is not a function.

x-intercept (p. 203)   The *x*-coordinate of a point where a graph crosses the *x*-axis.

Intercepto en x (p. 203)   Coordenada *x* por donde la gráfica cruza el eje de las *x*.

Example   The *x*-intercept of $3x + 4y = 12$ is 4.

y-intercept (p. 186)   The *y*-coordinate of a point where a graph crosses the *y*-axis.

Intercepto en y (p. 186)   Coordenada *y* por donde la gráfica cruza el eje de las *y*.

Example   The *y*-intercept of $y = 5x + 2$ is 2.

Index

A

absolute value, 429, 543

absolute value equations and inequalities, 80–89, 93, 95

absolute value functions, 219–224, 227

accuracy, measurements and, 49–51

Activity Lab
  accuracy and measurement, 49–51
  mean absolute deviation, 388–389
  paper folding and reflections, 505–506
  proving slope criteria, 575–578
  symmetry, 523–528
  tracing paper transformations, 493–494
  unit analysis, 44–48
  using residuals, 411–413

addition
  Angle Addition Postulate, 462
  of fractions, 1
  function operations, 337, 338
  segment addition postulate, 452
  solving systems by, 247

algebra, connecting with geometry
  areas of parallelograms and triangles, 559–567, 586
  areas of trapezoids, rhombuses, and kites, 568–574, 587
  Chapter Review, 586–587
  partitioning a segment, 557–558
  perimeter and area in the coordinate plane, 545–556, 586
  polygons in the coordinate plane, 579–585, 587
  proving slope criteria, 575–578
  Pull It All Together, 588

altitude, of a parallelogram, 559

Angle Addition Postulate, 462

angle bisectors, 471

angle of rotation, 515

angle pairs, 466–474, 489

angles, measuring, 430, 458–465, 488

applications
  admissions, 294
  aerial photography, 440
  agriculture, 218, 246
  airports, 259
  analyzing advertising revenue, 228
  analyzing sales data, 368
  aquariums, 362
  archaeology, 324

architecture, 22, 440
art, 246, 276
athletics, 109
aviation, 130
banking, 88, 236
baseball, 32, 419, 555
basketball, 398
bicycle rentals, 359
bike path, 216
biking, 88
biology, 59, 68, 88, 257, 340
blogs, 164
boating, 261
boiling point, 201
bowling, 19
business, 23, 28, 261, 267, 277, 278, 318, 408
cafeterias, 151
carpentry, 266
car rentals, 134
carwashes, 142
cell phone plans, 236
cell phones, 307
chemistry, 78, 79, 261
clothing, 207
coins, 245
collect calls, 362
college enrollment, 310
commissions, 68
computer animation, 503
computers, 193, 299
construction, 33, 347
cooking, 20
credit, 318
demographics, 343
dining out, 20
driving, 274
earnings, 274, 328
ecology, 324
electric cars, 108
electricity, 58, 182
employment, 13, 269
entertainment, 262, 404
environment, 294
exchange rates, 43
exercises, 280
falling objects, 124
family trip, 62
farm maintenance, 88
finance, 292
fireworks, 246
florists, 56
food drive, 328
foreign languages, 415
forestry, 202
fountains, 116
freight handling, 69
fuel, 140
fuel use, 395
fundraisers, 211, 340
furniture, 249
garages, 151
gardening, 17, 34, 56, 108, 554

gift certificates, 276
groceries, 270
half-life, 308
health clubs, 27
heart rates, 79
hiking, 237
history, 439, 514, 567
home maintenance, 554
horizons, 362
hummingbirds, 306
insects, 59
interest rates, 320, 321
interior design, 584
Internet traffic, 287
investments, 257
kayaking, 259
landscaping, 503
language arts, 521
lawn game, 11
literature, 465
maintenance, 40
manufacturing, 88, 290, 340, 343, 387, 439
medicine, 318
metallurgy, 573
mixed nuts, 262
money, 261
movies, 109, 424
moving expenses, 19
music, 57, 377
music stores, 270
news, 415
number theory, 157, 262
nutrition, 79, 140, 253
oil production, 88
online video games, 19
optics, 474
packaging, 398
painting, 20
parade floats, 59
parking garages, 361
parks, 32, 348
part-time jobs, 69
pet care, 556
photographs, 328
physics, 78, 138, 183
physiology, 10
polling, 88
population, 38, 287, 313, 321, 409
postage, 359
printing, 26
profits, 174, 307, 343
programming a video game, 542
projectors, 134
recipes, 42
rental rates, 67
running, 38
sales, 381
savings, 20
schedules, 58
science, 35, 332, 336
shirt colors, 424

shopping, 41, 138
skiing, 27, 102
sporting goods, 123, 342
sports, 211, 307, 316, 352, 382, 574
statistics, 58
surveys, 420
talent shows, 248
technology, 465
telecommunications, 450
test grades, 327
text message plans, 423
theme parks, 403
tiling, 554
time, 465
tips, 134
tournament locations, 428
track, 102
track and field, 246
transportation, 156
travel, 14, 27, 387, 481, 501
triathlons, 361
urban design, 563
urban planning, 216
vacations, 253
video downloads, 58
video games, 207
wages, 129
water, 307
weather, 35
whales, 133
wildlife management, 292, 387
wind or current problems, 258

area
  finding the area of a plot of land, 588
  of irregular shapes, 551, 562
  of parallelograms and triangles, 559–567, 586
  perimeter and area in the coordinate plane, 545–556, 586
  of a rectangle, 559
  of trapezoids, rhombuses, and kites, 568–574, 587

arithmetic sequences, 146–157, 163, 165
  Fibonacci sequence, 158–160
  rate of change and slope, 175

assessment
  Chapter Review, 90–93, 161–163, 225–227, 278–279, 363–367, 425–427, 487–489, 540–541, 586–587
  Got It?, 4, 5, 6, 7, 12, 13, 14, 15, 16, 21, 22, 23, 24, 29, 30, 31, 32, 37–38, 39, 40, 52, 54, 55, 60, 61, 62, 63, 71, 72, 73, 75, 80, 81, 82, 83, 84, 97, 98, 99, 103, 105, 111, 112, 113, 117, 118, 120, 121, 129, 130, 131, 135, 136, 137, 138, 139, 146, 148, 149, 151, 152, 153, 167, 169, 170, 171, 176, 177, 178, 179, 187, 188, 189, 190, 196, 197, 198, 204, 205, 206, 213,

214, 215, 219, 220, 221, 222, 231, 232, 233, 240, 241, 242, 243, 247, 248, 249, 250, 251, 256, 257, 258, 263, 264, 265, 266, 267, 271, 272, 273, 284, 285, 286, 287, 292, 293, 294, 295, 296, 301, 302, 303, 310, 311, 312, 313, 314, 323, 324, 325, 330, 331, 332, 333, 338, 339, 340, 345, 346, 347, 348, 349, 355, 356, 357, 358, 359, 371, 372, 374, 375, 380, 381, 382, 383, 384, 393, 394, 395, 400, 402, 404, 405, 406, 415, 416, 418, 431, 432, 433, 434, 442, 443, 445, 446, 452, 453, 454, 459, 461, 462, 467, 468, 470, 471, 476, 477, 478, 479, 496, 497, 498, 499, 500, 508, 509, 510, 511, 516, 517, 518, 533, 535, 536, 546, 547, 548, 549, 550, 560, 562, 568, 569, 570, 580, 581
  Open-Ended exercises, 11, 20, 28, 35, 59, 68, 88, 102, 116, 128, 133, 142, 156, 159, 173, 174, 217, 236, 261, 276, 290, 306, 318, 327, 328, 335, 343, 352, 438, 449, 450, 465, 482, 503, 514, 539, 566

B

base, of a parallelogram, 559
Big Ideas
  coordinate geometry, 492, 544
  data collection and analysis, 370
  data representation, 370
  equivalence, 2, 282
  function, 96, 166, 282
  measurements, 430, 544
  modeling, 96, 230, 370
  proportionality, 166
  reasoning, 430
  solving equations and inequalities, 2, 230
  transformations, 492
  visualization, 430

box-and-whisker plots, 370, 392–398, 426

brackets, 74
break-even points, 256

C

calculators. *See* graphing calculators
causal relationships, 405
Challenge exercises, 11, 20, 28, 36, 43, 59, 69, 79, 89, 102, 109, 116, 124, 134, 143, 157, 175, 183, 194, 202, 211, 218, 224, 237, 246, 254, 262, 270, 277, 290, 300, 308, 318, 328, 336, 343, 353, 362, 378, 387,

410, 424, 440, 450, 457, 465, 474, 482, 504, 514, 522, 556, 574

Chapter Review, 90–93, 161–163, 225–227, 278–279, 363–367, 425–427, 487–489, 540–541, 586–587

Choose a Method exercises, 42
circles, area of, 550
circumference, 546, 547
collinear points, 442
combining functions, 366
Compare and Contrast exercises
  34, 87, 141, 173, 210, 217, 223, 246, 253, 351, 361, 408, 422, 438, 448, 456, 521, 553
compositions of isometries, 532–539, 541
compound inequalities, 70–79, 93
compound interest, 311
Concept Summary
  finding information from a diagram, 468
  graphs of direct variations, 179
  linear and nonlinear functions, 110
  linear equations, 207
  slopes of lines, 171
  solving equations, 25
  solving linear systems, 255
  systems of linear equations, 234

conditional relative frequency, 418
congruent angles, 461
congruent segments, 453
continuous graphs, 119, 120–121
conversion factors, 38, 39, 40
coordinate geometry, 509
Coordinate Geometry exercises, 450, 474, 481, 504, 522, 540, 555, 556, 566, 573, 585
coordinate plane
  formulas and, 579
  midpoint and distance in, 475–482
  perimeter and area in 545–556, 586
  polygons in, 579–585, 587
  rotation in, 517
coplanar points and lines, 442
correlation coefficient *r*, 404
correlations, 400, 405
Critical Thinking exercises, 335
Cross Products Property, 53, 54
Cross Products Property of a Proportion, 53
cube root functions, 356
cumulative frequency tables, 375

D

data analysis
> box-and-whisker plots, 392–398, 426
> central tendency and dispersion, 370, 379–387, 425
> Chapter Review, 425–427
> finding information from a diagram, 468–469
> frequency and histograms, 370, 371–378, 425
> mean absolute deviation, 388–389
> Pull It All Together, 428
> scatter plots and trend lines, 370, 399–410, 426
> standard deviation, 390–391
> two-way frequency tables, 370, 414–424, 427
> using residuals, 411–413

data representation, 370

data sets, 393

data values, finding, 381

decimals, 1, 16

defined terms, 443

denominators, 55, 349

density, 35

dependent variables, 103

deviation, 388–389, 390–391

diagrams, finding information from, 468–469

dimensional analysis. *See* unit analysis

dimensions, missing, 560

direct variation, linear functions and, 176–183, 225

discrete graphs, 119, 120–121

dispersion, measures of, 379–391, 425

distance, in 3 dimensions, 482

distance formula, 477, 478–479

Distributive Property, 3–11, 14, 62–63, 90, 369

division
> function operations, 337, 339
> of real numbers, 369

Division Property of Equality, 14

Division Property of Square Roots, 348

domain
> linear functions, 166
> ranges and, 139–140, 281
> relations and functions, 135

E

elimination method, 247–254, 255, 279

endpoints, 477

equations. *See also* inequalities
> absolute value equations, 80–89, 95
> absolute value equations and inequalities, 93
> compound inequalities, 70–79
> Concept Summary, 25
> distributive property, 3–11
> exponential equations, 322–328, 365
> functions and, 95
> graphing, 184–185
> graphing functions and solving equations, 125–128
> linear equations, 186–194, 195–202, 203–211, 226, 229, 231
> literal equations and formulas, 29–36, 91
> of parallel lines, 213
> ratios, rates, and conversions, 37–43
> solving, 429, 543
> solving multi-step equations, 12–20, 95
> solving multi-step inequalities, 60–69
> solving one-variable equations, 296
> solving proportions, 52–59
> two-variable equations, 165
> using tables to write, 198
> with variables on both sides, 21–28, 91
> writing a direct variation equation, 177
> writing an equation from two points, 189
> writing an equation of a perpendicular line, 215
> writing equations of a trend line,402
> writing equations of horizontal translations, 222
> writing equations of vertical translations, 221
> writing from a graph, 188
> writing in point-slope form, 196
> writing in slope-intercept form, 187

equations and inequalities, systems of
> applications of linear systems, 255–262, 279
> Chapter Review, 278–279
> linear inequalities and, 263–271, 279
> Pull It All Together, 280
> solving by graphing, 231–237, 278
> solving using elimination, 247–254, 279
> solving using substitution, 240–246, 278
> solving using tables and graphs, 238–239
> systems of linear inequalities, 271–277, 279

equivalence, 2, 282

Error Analysis exercises, 10, 19, 27, 35, 43, 48, 58, 67, 69, 77, 88, 102, 115, 123, 133, 142, 155, 173, 182, 193, 210, 224, 236, 245, 253, 269, 276, 289, 298, 306, 307, 316, 327, 335, 342, 343, 352, 361, 378, 386, 397, 408, 423, 439, 456, 457, 464, 473, 480, 502, 512, 520, 522, 528, 538, 553, 583

Essential Understanding, 3, 6, 12, 21, 29, 37, 52, 60, 70, 80, 97, 103, 110, 117, 123, 129, 135, 146, 167, 176, 186, 195, 203, 212, 219, 231, 240, 247, 255, 263, 271, 283, 291, 301, 309, 322, 329, 337, 344, 355, 357, 371, 379, 392, 399, 414, 431, 441, 451, 458, 466, 475, 495, 507, 515, 532, 545, 559, 568, 569, 579,

estimation, 1, 43, 555

even and odd functions, 144–145

even functions, 144

exchange rates, 43

explicit formulas, 150, 152–153, 331

exponential equations, 322–328, 365

exponential expressions, 285, 286, 287

exponential functions, 291–300, 363
> comparing linear and exponential functions, 282, 301–308, 364
> writing, 314

exponential growth and decay, 309–318, 364

exponents, 283–290, 319–321, 363

expressions
> evaluating, 95, 281, 543
> rewriting fraction expressions, 4–5
> simplifying, 4, 6–8, 429, 543

extrapolation, 401

F

factors
> greatest common factors, 1
> perfect-square factors, 345
> variable factors, 345

Fibonacci sequence, 158–160

formulas
> and the coordinate plane, 579
> distance formula, 477, 478–479
> explicit formulas, 150, 152–153, 331
> inequalities and, 61

literal equations and, 31–32, 91
midpoint formulas, 475
recursive formulas, 149–150
rewriting, 32–33
slope formula, 170, 174

fractions
adding and subtracting, 1
decimals and, 1, 281
rewriting fraction expressions, 4–5
simplifying, 1
simplifying within radicals, 348
solving multi-step equations, 15

frequency and histograms, 371–378, 425

frequency tables, 371–372, 375

function notation, 137

function rules
graphing, 117–124, 162, 369
writing, 113–114, 129–134, 163, 491

functions, 96, 166, 282. *See also* equations; graphs and graphing
arithmetic sequences, 146–157, 163
Chapter Review, 161–163
combining, 282, 337–343
evaluating, 137–138
even and odd functions, 144–145
exponential functions, 282, 291–300, 363
Fibonacci sequence, 158–160
formalizing relations and functions, 135–143, 163
graphing a function rule, 117–124, 162, 165
modeling, 190
patterns and linear functions, 103–109, 161
patterns and nonlinear functions, 110–116, 162
radical and piecewise functions, 354–362, 367
step functions, 358, 359
Technology Lab, 125–128, 144–145
using graphs to relate two quantities, 97–102, 161
using properties of exponents to transform functions, 319–321
vocabulary, 96
writing, 229
writing a function rule, 129–134, 163
writing geometric sequences as, 333

G

geometric formulas, 31–32
geometric relationships, 103–104
geometric sequences, 282, 329–336, 365

geometry, connecting with algebra
areas of parallelograms and triangles, 559–567, 586
areas of trapezoids, rhombuses, and kites, 568–574, 587
Chapter Review, 586–587
partitioning a segment, 557–558
perimeter and area in the coordinate plane, 545–556, 586
polygons in the coordinate plane, 579–585, 587
proving slope criteria, 575–578
Pull It All Together, 586–587

Get Ready!, 1, 95, 165, 229, 281, 369, 429, 491, 543

glide reflections, 536

golden ratio, 133

graphing calculators
comparing linear and exponential functions, 308
correlation coefficients, 404
even and odd functions, 144
graphing an equation, 184–185
graphing equations, 210
graphing functions and solving equations, 125–126
line of best fit, 410

graphs and graphing
continuous and discrete graphs, 119, 120–121
continuous graphs, 119, 120–121
discrete graphs, 119, 120–121
exponential functions, 293
exponential models, 294, 295
function rules, 369
functions and, 95
graphing absolute value functions, 219–224
graphing a direct variation equation, 178, 179
graphing a function rule, 162, 165
graphing a horizontal translation, 222
graphing an equation, 184–185
graphing a reflection image, 509
graphing a vertical translation, 220
graphing cube root functions, 356
graphing functions and solving equations, 125–128
graphing lines, 204, 205
linear inequalities, 264–266
piecewise functions, 357
rate of change and slope, 168, 169
solving exponential equations by, 325
solving linear systems, 255
solving systems by, 231–237, 278
solving systems by tables and graphs, 238–239

square root functions, 355
systems of linear inequalities, 271–272
translating, 491
using point-slope form, 196
using to relate two quantities, 97–102, 161
writing an equation from, 188
writing an inequality from a graph, 267

greatest common factors, 1

H

histograms, 370, 371–378, 425
History of Math, golden ratio, 133
horizontal lines, 171, 205
horizontal translations, 222

I

identities
with no solution, 24, 27
solving equations and, 229

images, 495, 497
glide reflections, 536
rotation images, 516
of translations, 498

independent variables, 103

inequalities. *See also* equations and inequalities, systems of
absolute value equations and inequalities, 93
absolute value inequalities, 80–89
compound inequalities, 70–79, 93
with no solution, 64, 65
solutions of, 263
solving equations and inequalities, 2, 229
solving multi-step inequalities, 60–69, 92

infinity, 74
intercepts, 204
interpolation, 401
intersecting lines, 534, 535
intersections, of points, lines, and planes, 444
interval notation, 74, 75
irregular shapes, area of, 551, 562
isometric drawings, 433–435
isometries, compositions of, 532–539, 541
isosceles trapezoids, 483

J

joint relative frequency, 416

K

Key Concepts

absolute value equations, 81
absolute value inequalities, 83
angle pairs, 466–467
angles, 458, 460
area of a parallelogram, 559
area of a rectangle, 559
area of a trapezoid, 568
area of a triangle, 561
arithmetic sequences, 150
compositions of isometries, 532
continuous and discrete
graphs, 119
cube root functions, 356
defined terms, 443
distance formula, 477
exponential decay, 312
exponential functions, 291
exponential growth, 309
finding slope of lines, 171
formulas and the coordinate
plane, 579
function operations, 337
geometric sequences, 329
graphing a direct variation
equation, 179
linear and nonlinear
functions, 110
linear equations, 207
mean, median, and mode, 379
midpoint formulas, 475
perimeter, circumference, and
area, 545
point-slope form, 195
property of a proportion, 53
reflection across a line, 508
reflections across intersecting
lines, 534
reflections across parallel
lines, 533
rhombuses and kites, 569
rotation in the coordinate
plane, 517
rotations about a point, 515
slope formula, 170
slopes of parallel lines, 212
slopes of perpendicular lines, 213
solving equations, 25
solving exponential equations
with the same base, 322
solving linear systems, 255
square root functions, 354
systems of linear equations, 234
translations, 498
undefined terms, 441
zero and negative exponents, 283

kites, 483, 544, 568–574, 587

L

least common multiple, 1

Lesson Check, 8–10, 16–18,
25–26, 33–34, 41–42, 56–57,
65–67, 76–77, 85–87,

100–101, 106–108, 114–115,
122–123, 132–133, 140–142,
154–155, 172–173, 180–181,
191–193, 199–201, 208–209,
216–217, 223–224, 234–235,
243–245, 252, 259–261,
268–269, 274–275, 288–289,
297–298, 304–306, 315–316,
326–327, 334–335, 341–342,
350–351, 360–361, 376–377,
385–386, 396–397, 407–408,
421–422, 436–438, 447–448,
455–456, 463–464, 472–473,
479–480, 501–502, 512–513,
519–521, 537–538, 552–553,
564–565, 571–573, 583

Lesson Lab

Fibonacci sequence, 158–160
partitioning a segment, 557–558
standard deviation, 390–391
using properties of exponents to
transform functions, 319–321

like terms, 7–8, 12–13

linear equations, 186. *See also*
linear functions
forms of, 226
graphing, 190, 229
point-slope form, 195–202
slope-intercept form, 186–194
standard form, 203–211
systems of linear equations, 231

linear functions

absolute value functions, 227
Chapter Review, 225–227
comparing linear and exponential
functions, 301–308, 364
direct variation, 176–183, 225
forms of linear equations, 226
graphing absolute value
functions, 219–224
patterns and, 103–109
point-slope form, 195–202
Pull It All Together, 228
rate of change and slope,
167–175, 225
slope-intercept form, 186–194
slopes of parallel and
perpendicular lines,
212–218, 226
standard form, 203–211
Technology Lab, 184–185

linear inequalities, 263–270, 279
systems of, 271–277, 279

Linear Pair Postulate, 469

linear parent functions, 186

linear systems, applications of,
255–262, 279

line of best fit, 404, 411, 412

lines, *See also* linear equations,
linear functions, parallel lines,
perpendicular lines
classifying, 214
finding slope of, 171
graphing, 204, 205

points, lines, and planes,
441–450, 487
proving slope criteria for parallel
and perpendicular lines,
575–578
reflections across a line, 508
reflections across intersecting
lines, 534, 535
reflections across parallel
lines, 533

line symmetry, 523

literal equations, 29–36, 91

Look for a Pattern exercises, 156,
182, 352

Looking Ahead Vocabulary, 1, 95,
165, 229, 281, 369, 429, 491,
543

M

Make a Conjecture, 159, 531

mapping diagrams, 135

marginal relative frequency, 416

mean, 379

**mean absolute deviation
(MAD),** 388–389

measurements
accuracy and, 49–51
Big Ideas, 544
measuring angles, 430,
458–465, 488
measuring segments, 430,
451–457, 488
ratios, rates, and conversions, 43

**measures of central tendency and
dispersion,** 370, 379–387,
425

median of a data set, 379

Mental Math, 6, 9, 43, 68, 289

**midpoint and distance in the
coordinate plane,** 430,
475–482, 489

midpoints, 36, 454–455

mode, 379

modeling, 96, 230, 370
data analysis, 370
exponential decay, 313
exponential growth, 310
exponential models, 294, 295
systems of equations, 230

**More Practice and Problem
Solving Exercises,** 10, 11,
19–20, 27–28, 35–36, 42–43,
55–56, 58–59, 67–69, 77, 78–79,
87, 101–102, 108–109, 116,
123–124, 133–134, 142–143,
156–157, 174–175, 182–183,
193–194, 201–202, 210–211,
218, 224, 236–237, 245–246,
253–254, 261–262, 269–270,
276–277, 289–290, 298–300,
306–308, 316–318, 327–328,

335–336, 342–343, 352–353, 361–362, 377–378, 387, 398, 408–410, 423–424, 438–440, 449–450, 456–457, 464–465, 473–474, 481–482, 503–504, 513–514, 521–522, 538–539, 554–556, 565–567, 573–574, 584–585

Multiple Representations exercises, 438, 440

multiples, 1

multiplication
function operations, 337, 339
multiplying two radical expressions, 346
of real numbers, 369
solving systems by, 249–250

Multiplication Property, 5–6, 52–53

Multiplication Property of Equality, 53

Multiplication Property of Square Roots, 344

multi-step equations, solving, 12–20, 90, 95

multi-step inequalities, 60–69, 92

multi-step proportions, 54–55

N

nets and drawings, 430, 431–440, 487

nonlinear functions
patterns and, 110–116
writing a function rule, 131

nonlinear trends, 406

number theory, 157

numerators, 55

O

odd functions, 144

one-variable equations, 296

Open-Ended exercises, 11, 20, 28, 35, 59, 68, 88, 102, 116, 128, 133, 142, 156, 157, 159, 173, 174, 211, 217, 236, 253, 261, 318, 327, 328, 335, 343, 352, 361, 398, 438, 449, 450, 465, 482, 503, 514, 522, 538, 555, 566, 573

opposite orientations, 507

opposite reciprocals, 214

order of operations, 281

orthographic drawings, 435–436

P

paper folding and reflections, 505–506

parallel lines, 212–218, 533, 575–578

parallelograms, 483, 544, 559–567, 586

parent function, 186

parentheses, 74

patterns
and linear functions, 103–109, 161
and nonlinear functions, 110–116, 162
zero and negative exponents, 289

pentagons, 549

percent change, finding, 281

percentile ranks, 395

perfect-square factors, 345

perimeter, 544, 545–556, 586

perpendicular bisectors, 507

perpendicular lines, 212–218, 575–578

piecewise functions, 357–359

planes
midpoint and distance in the coordinate plane, 475–482
points, lines, and planes, 441–450, 487
rotation in the coordinate plane, 517

points
finding slope using, 170, 174
writing an equation from two, 189
writing an equation from two points, 197

points, lines, and planes, 430, 441–450, 487
reflection across a line, 508
rotations about a point, 515

point-slope form, 195–202

polygons, 483–486, 491, 544, 579–585, 587

postulates
Angle Addition Postulate, 462
Linear Pair Postulate, 469
points, lines, and planes, 444, 446
Protractor Postulate, 460
Ruler Postulate, 451
Segment Addition Postulate, 452

Power of a Product Property, 319

Power of a Quotient Property, 319

powers, simplifying, 284

preimages, 495

probability, 566

Product of a Powers Property, 319

properties
Cross Products Property of a Proportion, 53

Distributive Property, 3–11, 14, 62–63, 90, 369
Division Property of Square Roots, 348
Multiplication Property of Square Roots, 344
properties of reflections, 511
properties of rotations, 518

proportions, 52–59, 92, 166

Protractor Postulate, 460

Pull It All Together, 84, 164, 228, 280, 368, 428, 490, 542, 588

Q

quadrilaterals, 581

quadrilaterals and other polygons, 483–486

quartiles, 392, 393

Quotient of Powers Property, 319

R

radicals
radical functions, 354–362, 367
simplifying, 344–353, 366

range
domain and, 139–140, 281
of functions, 138–139
measures of central tendency and dispersion, 382, 383
relations and functions, 135

rates, 37–38, 40–41

rates of change, 303
and slope, 167–175, 225

ratios, rates, and conversions, 37–43, 92

rays, naming, 443

Reasoning exercises, 10, 14, 18, 21, 28, 29–30, 40, 42, 43, 57, 63, 66, 67, 69, 77, 79, 86, 88, 99, 101, 102, 104, 105, 107, 108, 109, 111, 116, 124, 128, 130, 131, 133, 134, 139, 142, 143, 145, 150, 151, 155, 156, 157, 169, 175, 181, 182, 185, 188, 192, 198, 201, 206, 209, 210, 218, 220, 235, 236, 237, 246, 252, 253, 254, 258, 260, 261, 262, 269, 270, 275, 290, 298, 300, 303, 307, 308, 313, 316, 317, 326, 346, 352, 362, 374, 378, 381, 386, 387, 395, 397, 398, 400, 402, 404, 409, 410, 418, 420, 422, 424, 432, 446, 448, 449, 450, 454, 459, 470, 474, 478, 480, 481, 482, 486, 502, 503, 514, 519, 521, 522, 531, 535, 539, 550, 551, 555, 566, 572, 573, 584

rectangles, 483, 546, 559

recursive formulas, 149–150, 194, 331

reflectional symmetry, 523

reflection rules, 510

reflections, 507–514, 540
  glide reflections, 536
  paper folding and reflections, 505–506
  reflections across intersecting lines, 534, 535
  reflections across parallel lines, 533

relations and functions, formalizing, 135–143, 163

relative frequency, 416

residuals, using, 411–413

rhombuses, 483, 544, 568–574, 587

riddles, solving, 487

rigid motions, 495, 496

rotational symmetry, 523

rotations, 515–522, 541

ruler postulate, 451

rules
  function rules, 113–114, 117–124, 129–134, 162, 163, 369, 491
  reflection rules, 510
  writing to describe translations, 499–500

S

scatter plots and trend lines, 399–410, 411–413, 426

segment addition postulate, 452

segment bisectors, 454

segments
  measuring, 430, 451–457, 488
  midpoint and distance in the coordinate plane, 475–482
  naming, 443
  partitioning, 557–558

sequences
  arithmetic sequences, 146
  Fibonacci sequence, 158–160
  geometric sequences, 329–336

skewed histograms, 373

slope criteria, proving, 575–578

slope formula, 169, 174

slope-intercept form, 186–194

slopes
  finding using points, 170
  of parallel and perpendicular lines, 212–218, 226
  point-slope form, 195–202
  rate of change and slope, 167–175, 225
  slope-intercept form, 186–194

solids, drawing a net from, 432

solutions
  absolute value equations without, 82
  identities and equations without, 24, 27
  indentifying constraints and viable solutions, 257
  of inequalities, 263
  inequalities without, 64, 65
  inequalities with special solutions, 64–65
  solving systems by elimination and, 251
  substitution method and, 243
  systems with infinite, 233
  systems without, 233

special solutions, 64–65

spreadsheets, 28

square roots, 344, 348, 354, 355

squares, 483

squaring numbers, 429, 543

standard deviation, 390–391

standard form, 203–211

Statistics exercises, 58

STEM, 10, 22, 33, 35, 48, 59, 68, 78, 79, 88, 108, 124, 138, 182, 183, 201, 257, 261, 287, 290, 318, 332, 336, 387, 398, 503

step functions, 358, 359

substitution method
  solving linear systems, 255
  solving systems by, 230, 240–246, 278

subtraction
  of fractions, 1
  function operations, 337, 338
  solving systems by, 248

surface area, 36

symmetric histograms, 373

symmetry, 523–528

systems, of linear inequalities, 271–277, 279. *See also* equations and inequalities, systems of

T

tables
  frequency and histograms, 370, 371–378, 425
  functions and, 95
  and graphs, 98–99
  rate of change and slope, 167
  scatter plots and trend lines, 399–410, 426
  solving systems by, 238–239
  two-way frequency tables, 414–424, 427
  writing a direct variation equation, 179
  writing equations and, 198

Take Note, 3, 25, 53, 81, 83, 110, 119, 150, 170, 171, 179, 195, 207, 212, 213, 234, 255, 283, 291, 309, 312, 322, 329, 337, 354, 356, 379, 441, 443, 444, 446, 451, 458, 460, 466, 467, 468, 469, 475, 477, 498, 508, 515, 517, 532, 533, 534, 545, 559, 561, 568, 569, 579

Technology Lab
  even and odd functions, 144–145
  exploring multiple transformations, 529–531
  graphing functions and solving equations, 125–128
  linear functions, 184–185
  solving systems by tables and graphs, 238–239

term of a sequence, 146

Think About a Plan exercises, 11, 19, 27, 35, 42, 58, 67, 78, 87, 101, 108, 116, 124, 134, 142, 156, 174, 193, 201, 210, 218, 224, 236, 246, 253, 261, 269, 276, 289, 299, 306, 317, 327, 335, 352, 361, 378, 387, 398, 409, 423, 439, 449, 457, 464, 473, 481, 503, 513, 522, 538, 554, 565, 573, 584

tracing paper transformations, 493–494

transformations
  Chapter Review, 540–541
  compositions of isometries, 532–539, 541
  exploring multiple transformations, 529–531
  paper folding and reflections, 505–506
  Pull It All Together, 542
  reflections, 492, 507–514, 540
  rotations, 492, 515–522, 541
  symmetry, 523–528
  tracing paper transformations, 493–494
  translations, 492, 495–504, 540

translations, 219, 220, 221, 222, 540

trapezoids, 483, 544, 568–574, 587

trend lines
  scatter plots and, 399–410, 426
  writing equations of, 402

triangles, 548, 559–567, 580, 586

tripods, 446

two-step equations, 95

two-variable equations, 165

two-way frequency tables, 414–424, 427

U

undefined terms, 441

uniform histograms, 373

unit analysis, 38–39

unit rates, 37–38, 165, 369

V

variable factors, 7, 345

variables
  linear functions, 174
  literal equations, 30–31
  patterns and linear functions, 103
  rate of change and slope, 167
  solving equations with variables
    on both sides, 21–28
  solving inequalities and, 63–64
  solving one-variable equations,
    296
  substitution method and, 241

vertical lines, 171, 205

vertical line tests, 136–137

vertical shifts, 295

vertical translations, 220, 221

visualization, as Big Idea, 430

Visualization exercises
  areas of trapezoids, rhombuses,
    and kites, 574
  measuring segments, 457
  nets and drawings, 440

vocabulary
  exercises, 26, 34, 42, 57, 77, 107,
    115, 123, 133, 141, 155, 173,
    181, 192, 200, 209, 217, 235,
    244, 252, 260, 268, 275, 288,
    298, 305, 316, 351, 360, 377,
    386, 397, 408, 422, 438, 448,
    456, 464, 472, 502, 512, 520,
    527, 538, 564, 572
  Looking Ahead Vocabulary, 1, 95,
    165, 229, 281, 369, 429,
    491, 543

W

writing
  direct variation, 182
  elimination method, 252
  an explicit formula, 151
  exponential functions, 314
  functions, 229
  linear inequalities, 269
  piecewise functions, 358
  radical expressions, 347
  solving systems by graphing, 235
  substitution method and,
    245, 246
  systems of equations, 232
  systems of inequalities from a
    graph, 272–273
  writing a direct variation
    equation, 177
  writing a direct variation from a
    table, 179

  writing a function rule, 113–114,
    163, 491
  writing an equation from a
    graph, 188
  writing a reflection rule, 510
  writing a rule to describe
    translations, 499–500
  writing geometric sequences as
    functions, 333

Writing exercises, 11, 19, 26,
    36, 43, 68, 71, 77, 87, 116,
    123, 133, 193, 210, 275,
    300, 327, 341, 342, 351,
    377, 378, 389, 398, 408,
    412, 422, 423, 440, 450,
    457, 474, 504, 522, 528,
    539, 553, 554, 565, 566,
    574, 583

X

x-intercepts, 203

Y

y-intercepts, 203

Z

zero and negative
    exponents, 282,
    283–290, 363

Acknowledgments

Staff Credits

The people who made up the High School Mathematics team—representing composition services, core design digital and multimedia production services, digital product development, editorial, editorial services, manufacturing, marketing, and production management—are listed below.

Patty Fagan, Suzanne Finn, Matt Frueh, Cynthia Harvey, Linda Johnson, Roshni Kutty, Cheryl Mahan, Eve Melnechuk, Cynthia Metallides, Hope Morley, Michael Oster, Wynnette Outland, Brian Reardon, Matthew Rogers, Ann-Marie Sheehan, Kristen Siefers, Richard Sullivan, Susan Tauer, Mark Tricca, Oscar Vera, Paula Vergith

Additional Credits: Emily Bosak, Olivia Gerde, Alyse McGuire, Stephanie Mosely

Illustration

Jeff Grunewald: 101, 102, 134, 584; **Christopher Wilson:** 377; **Stephen Durke:** 439, 440, 450, 451, 464, 457, 479, 500, 556, 563; **Phil Guzy:** 525.

Technical Illustration

Aptara, Inc.; Datagrafix, Inc.; GGS Book Services

Photography

Every effort has been made to secure permission and provide appropriate credit for photographic material. The publisher deeply regrets any omission and pledges to correct errors called to its attention in subsequent editions.

Unless otherwise acknowledged, all photographs are the property of Pearson Education, Inc.

35, Reuters/Corbis; **158,** John Glover/Alamy Images; **158,** Bob Gibbons/Alamy Images; **352,** Laurie Neish/iStockphoto; **446,** Kelly Redinger/Alamy Images; **465,** Stuart Melvin/Alamy Images; **474,** Richard Menga/Fundamental Photographs; **514,** North Wind Picture Archives/Alamy Images; **522,** Alan Copson/City Pictures/Alamy Images.

Acknowledgments